Advance Praise for *Nothing is Free*

"The modern world of business has been dominated by an almost dogmatic belief that corporations exist to serve shareholders, first and foremost. Then a little book comes along that asks some very big questions that demand our thoughtful attention. Nothing is Free utilizes a delightful conversational approach that forces the reader to question the prevailing wisdom, and lays out an innovative and Christian perspective on how to enhance shareholder value. Business leaders will find in these pages a simple, yet profound basis for re-motivating the enterprise through personal virtue and a commitment to being the company God intended it to be."

–**John Menghini**, Chairman, Veritas Partners

"Thought-provoking, challenging, refreshing. Nothing is Free gracefully makes the case that business guided by virtue (God) is the recipe for true and long-lasting stakeholder value."

–**John Joerger**, Director – Global Transportation & International Trade Compliance, Garmin International

"Dave Geenens does an amazing job articulating how the level of government intervention is inversely proportional to the level of virtues practiced in business. It is absolutely brilliant! This book is sensational; a must read.

–**Tim Haahs**, Founder and CEO, Tim Haahs Engineers and Architects

i

Nothing is Free

The Price Only Business Leaders Can Pay to Protect Free Markets

by Dave Geenens

First Edition, 2013
ISBN 0-9768210-2-1
10 9 8 7 6 5 4 3 2 1
Manufactured in the United States of America

Additional copies of this book are available to corporations, organizations, churches, and others at special institutional prices. For more information, please contact the publisher:

Inhance Press
303 Santa Fe Street
Atchison, Kansas 66002
www.inhanceleadership.com

Sources of Inspiration
for this Book Include ...

In his Encyclical, Caritas in Veritate, Pope Benedict XVI called for "a profoundly new way of understanding the business enterprise." He referred to "grave deviations and failures" along with a new cosmopolitan class of managers that has emerged who are often answerable only to shareholders.[1]

If you are not paying for something, you are not the customer.
–conventional Dutch wisdom

Two pigs were reflecting on their barnyard experience . . .
One said, 'I can't believe they're feeding us three meals a day!"
The other added, 'Yeah! And the roof over our head is free, too!"
(Think about it . . .)

"For the time is coming when people will not endure sound teaching, but having itching ears they will accumulate for themselves teachers to suit their own likings, and will turn away from listening to the truth and wander into myths."[2]

"The Church offers no models to present; models that are real and truly effective can only arise within the framework of different historical situations, through the efforts of all those who responsibly confront concrete problems in all their social, economic, political, and cultural aspects, and these with one another."[3]

–Blessed John Paul II

---

1 Benedict XVI, Caritas in Veritate, (Vatican: Libreria Editrice Vaticana, 2009), 40.
2 The Holy Bible, 2 Timothy 4:3-4, (RSV).
3 Blessed John Paul II, Encyclical Letter Centisimus Annus, 43.

Foreword

(intentionally left blank)

Author's Comments

One of the first lessons I learned in business was that nothing is free. Free freight? There is no such thing. That simply means that the cost of freight is covered by profit made elsewhere. Buy one, get one free? The cost of the second item is covered in the margin of the first one. Interest free? The cost of interest is absorbed in the profit made on the sale of the item. Nothing is free.

Having spent 26 years in the marketplace in a variety of positions, including numerous executive and three CEO roles, I was an active, unconscious participant in and beneficiary of the benefits of a free market. My participation and the corresponding rewards were achieved with little or no conscious consideration of the free market system in which the U.S. operates. The free market was there; our business operated serving customers; profits were made; rewards were shared; our collective creativity and innovation fueled continued success.

When I transitioned to academia a few years ago, I was introduced to the debate over the benefits or malevolence of business and free markets. I am not ignorant of the many missteps made by high-profile business leaders and the negative sentiment shared by many. I understand, but this seems so far away from what we were doing and my experience. I was aware of some of the political stances, but had chosen not to invest my time and energy in what I thought was wasteful activity. Like many, I had given up hope of changing anything in Washington.

My personal experience informed me that business does good. I had seen customers receive great value for their dollar. I had seen vendors grow and thrive through mutually beneficial partnerships. I had seen people grow and achieve their goals. I had seen people care for one another and work together toward something bigger than themselves. I had also seen the tough times when costs had to be controlled or cut, and people had to be let go or laid-off. In most cases, these circumstances were handled humanely and with compassion.

I began to read and study more about this debate. I was exposed to Catholic social teaching for the first time. I was already pretty well informed of Biblical truths related to commerce, wealth, and some of the pitfalls that can accompany a life and career in the marketplace.

Though my studies are not finished, I am confident in what I have read and learned. The push for understanding where the costs of a free market are covered (because nothing is free) and what I learned about Catholic social teaching led to the discovery of some profound truths.

The truths revealed in researching the Encyclical Letters from Rerum Novarum, written in 1892 by Pope Leo XIII, through Caritas in Veritate, written in 2009 by Pope Benedict XVI were not what I expected after listening to people who harbor negative sentiment toward business and free markets. This friction motivated me to study more.

The main stage in this fight as been hijacked by the politicians, when the real battle must be fought in business by business leaders. The push for government to intervene for the purpose of righting injustices observed versus the necessity to protect free markets has resulted in the polarizing of America significantly along political party lines.

I cannot reject the sentiment of those who doubt the goodness in business. They have certainly been exposed to the worst of it. But the Church is clear. There is one tool the State doesn't have: the actual reins of business for which business leaders are solely responsible. The primary responsibility for protecting human rights in the economic sector and the pursuit of that which serves all is that of the people, i.e. business people.

This has significant implications for all business leaders and for those invested in the polarizing arguments about free markets. I don't believe the real battle is about free markets. The real battle is about an institutionalized ideology and the price only business leaders can pay to protect free markets.

It is appropriate to acknowledge the doubts that many Americans have about the motivations and morals of politicians. Legislation passed by lawmakers to temper injustices observed in business can be likened to 'the pot calling the kettle black.' One of the book's early reviewers; someone I admire and respect; offered that politicians use a different currency (power vs. money) to achieve their ends; often having little to do with protecting the common good, but more to do with their own reelection to a seat of power.

This may be true, but here is precisely where the debate polarizes most people and meaningful progress stops. Sitting at the polar extremes and arguing rhetorically will get us nowhere. Perhaps there are lessons in this book that can help politicians reorient their moral compasses. There is no contributory negligence claim here. It is right and appropriate for business leaders to own what they need to own, claim the moral high ground, and then perhaps politician motives and character will be truly revealed. Certainly, without the easy scapegoat of business missteps and dominant ideology motivations, political agendas would be much easier to identify and rebuke. Someone else will have to develop a new model and write a book for lawmakers representing the people.

I struggled with how to best deliver the message in this book. Having been educated and inspired by other fables written by Ken Blanchard, Patrick Lencioni, and Eli Goldratt, among others, I decided on that medium of delivery; the product of which is this book.

I also want to make it easy for those interested in the Church's teachings and sources from where I drew the tenets represented in this book to read more. Accordingly, you'll find footnotes with detailed excerpts from key references. Yes, this is a story, but the tenets represented in and lived by the characters are true.

I hope you enjoy the story, learn from it, and transform the world with it.

"In economic matters, respect for human dignity
requires the practice of the virtue of temperance,
so as to moderate attachment to this world's goods;
the practice of the virtue of justice, to preserve our
neighbor's rights and render him what is his due ..."

(2Cor 8:9, RSV)[4]

4   Catechism of the Catholic Church, 2407.

Table of Contents

Prologue

Cupcakes and Coffee had been an instant success. Riding the wave of interest in the artistry and taste of the mini-cakes across the U.S., Rebecca Morton had been the first to hire a gourmet pastry chef, from France no less, to design and create the delicacies unique to Cupcakes and Coffee, expanding at a pace to match the growth of the market. By all measures, market and customer-related, no one made a more artistic, tastier treat than Cupcakes and Coffee. Gallop ranked Cupcakes and Coffee the top single-destination comfort food restaurant in the U.S. the last three years.

As success built on success, Rebecca had encouraged and overseen expanding their product offering beyond cupcakes to include breakfast crepes to target the morning business crowd, and to bagged, bite-sized brownies for the sure-to-come 3:00 pm snack cravers at the end of a long day. Gluten-free offerings in a handful of their top-selling cupcakes and bite-sized brownies made their product appeal even more universal.

The first Cupcakes and Coffee store was located in the quaint, industrial town of Atchison, Kansas. The downtown, and the entire town, really, was like a trip back a century ago when river boats traversing the Missouri River would stop to re-supply; giving their weary boarders a break from the sway and swoon of the waters of the Missouri. Travelers would shop and trade on the streets of Atchison, just like those who followed Lewis and Clark on their trail to the great northwest decades earlier. It was a thriving center of commerce for most of the 20th century, and had maintained much of its old-world charm. With a unique blend of hard-working industry workers, the many white-collar workers that accompany a rural county seat, a large farming and agricultural community, a vocational and technical school, and a four-year college campus in town, Atchison was the perfect place to launch Cupcakes and Coffee. In 2010, Rebecca Morton, with the support of her attorney husband, Rick, had done so.

Having learned the ropes of franchising as Manager, Regional

Manager, then Director of Franchise Operations in the southwest's mega-Mexican food chain Burrito Barn, her knowledge of franchising as a business model helped her expand the Cupcakes and Coffee brand quickly, while most of her competition remained one-store novelty shops. She recruited franchise owners, not only in large metropolitan areas like other franchisers, but targeted other smaller rural towns with old-world charm like Atchison.

Now at a scale that allowed for significant purchase volume, Rebecca had negotiated great pricing on all food commodity ingredients, significantly increasing margins on products sold. The large volume of coffee sold helped Rebecca make the decision to vertically integrate her coffee business by owning the coffee growing, roasting, and grinding supply chain for her stores.

Her business strategy worked, and the company's meteoric rise to prominence is the stuff of legends. With the best product, reputation, and highest profit margins in the market, Rebecca Morton took Cupcakes and Coffee public with an IPO on April 16, 2013. The opening share price of $15 per share made Rebecca one of three multi-millionaires in Atchison, Kansas; the latest in a long line of industry sages and success stories born in Atchison, raised in Atchison, and living the dream that comes with business success.

Celebrating the successful and lucrative IPO with a gourmet breakfast crepe and cup of coffee at the podium at the New York Stock Exchange - Rebecca was invited to ring-in the trading day as she was most-recently voted one of the top-ten woman CEO's in America by Forbes Magazine - Rebecca soaked up the applause and recognition that had come on the heels of the crazy, fast-paced, all-in ride that is starting a business from nothing to IPO in three years. Though happy and proud . . . her feet were killing her. She needed a break that, unfortunately, would not come until her return to Atchison that evening.

Our story begins here . . .

2

Part I

The Commute

"Mrs. Morton, please follow me. Your limousine is waiting. At 10:00 a.m., ABC is taping an interview with you for Good Morning America to be broadcast tomorrow morning. We must get moving in order to get you to the studios on time."

"That's right!" Rebecca recollected. Having been a fan and avid watcher of GMA for years, Rebecca's face lit up. "Who is doing the interview? Is it George? Josh? Oh please, let it be Josh," in a rare moment of adolescent amour.

"Let me look here . . . the network itinerary doesn't say . . . so we won't know until we get there. I can call if you wish?"

"Yes, please!" Her exuberance and excitement easily overcoming her foot pain as she kicked off her shoes sliding into the limo.

Sitting face-forward in the limousine, accompanied by Mark, the assigned network attaché for the day, Rebecca watched the hundreds of small retail shops and throngs of people zoom by from right to left as the limousine traveled the five miles to the ABC studios. Mark was listening intently as the phone began to ring on the other end.

"American Broadcasting Company, how may I help you?"

"Sharon, this is Mark Hansen. Good morning."

"Good morning, Mark! What can I do for you today?"

"Do you happen to know which GMA anchor is scheduled to do the Rebecca Morton interview this morning?"

With eyes raised as he listened for a response and Rebecca staring at his face anticipating an answer, Sharon responded, "Robin Roberts is scheduled to do that interview at 10:00 a.m." Mark shook his head.

"Robin Roberts."

Rebecca's eyes widened, "Are you kidding?! Robin Roberts! I love her! What an amazing woman! First overcoming breast cancer, then a bone marrow transplant . . ." Accolades continued to pour out of her mouth, as did a little smile. Her attention returned to the shops and people zooming by.

"Thank you, Sharon. Please alert the make-up team that we are ten minutes out. Uh huh. See you in ten."

With only a few traffic stops, rare in the Times Square area of Manhattan, the black limousine with privacy-protecting smoked glass, pulled up outside the ABC studios at 9:30 a.m. sharp. Mark, holding the door for Rebecca and helping her out of the limousine while she rushed to fit her French-manicured toes into the much-too-narrow pair of Prada stilettos, said, "Let me be the first to welcome you to ABC studios. We hope your experience with us is rewarding and memorable."

Sliding as lady-like as possible out of the back seat of the limousine, careful not to stretch or rip her knee-length skirt on the seatbelt buckles, she made it to the curb with a deep breath and smile, "Thank you, Mark. I am sure it will be." She gazed upward at the high-rise buildings surrounding the street, shielding the morning commuters from the bright morning sunshine. They entered ABC studios at a brisk walk.

"Good morning, Mr. Hansen."

"Good morning, Tammy. I'd like you to meet Mrs. Rebecca Morton, CEO of Cupcakes and Coffee."

"Oh, what a pleasure," standing up to shake Rebecca's hand. "We all love your mocha caramel volcano cupcake around here. The filling is incredible!"

"Thank you," responding with a blush of humility. "Nice to meet you. I'm Rebecca," extending her hand.

"This way," summoned Mark and grabbing her arm, "Your make-up team is waiting."

With a turn, a glance, and wink in the direction of Tammy, Rebecca mused, "I get someone to do my make-up for me today." They headed upstairs.

The Interview

"Three, two, one; we're live!"

"Good morning, America! It is my pleasure to introduce you to one of America's top female CEOs and the CEO of one of my favorite 'goody' places on earth, Cupcakes and Coffee, Rebecca Morton. Rebecca, welcome."

Still in awe that Robin Roberts was sitting across from her in a casual studio set at ABC in Manhattan, Rebecca smiled, "Thank you, Robin. It's a pleasure to be here."

"As one woman to another, how did you rise to such a prominent executive position as CEO of the largest 'goody' company in the United States in just three years? That must have been incredible!"

Rebecca grinned, "Well, it's easier when you start and own your own company. As you know, though, to be good at anything, it takes a lot of hard work. Nothing is easy. Nothing is free. You have to work for what you get. Early mornings, late nights, weekends; you know the

5

pace. But when you are passionate about what you do, most of the time it doesn't feel like work."

"Oh, yes, I know the pace, and you're right, it takes a lot to be successful in any career. I imagine that most women watching today are curious about how you, a professional woman, survived and excelled in a world and role historically dominated by men."

"I had some great male mentors in the business world early in my career. Some of the best advice I received was that you've got to think like, act like, and be like those with whom you want to belong. I learned if you want to reach the top, then you've got to be able to stand toe-to-toe with a man. I have learned to do just that. I've tried to anticipate a more competitive response to challenges, like a man. I've tried to push ideas and agendas more forcefully, like a man. Even though I have felt like screaming or crying at times, I have held it in, suppressed my emotions, and things have worked out. In my company, Cupcakes and Coffee, I try to deviate a little, though, from some of the advice I've been given. You know, add a bit of a woman's touch . . ."

Adjusting in her chair, Robin queried, "Tell us about that. What would you consider to be the most identifiable 'woman's touch' at Cupcakes and Coffee?"

Pausing for just a moment to reflect, Rebecca shared, "First of all, it's hard to change the spots on a leopard, and my training and experiences are like my spots. It's hard for me to be different. Results matter, man or woman. Shareholder wealth matters, man or woman. Sometimes business is rough and tumble. It's hard and it hurts at times. Something different . . .," placing her thumb and forefinger in a thinking pose on the right side of her face, she continued, "When possible, I try to listen more to my employees and franchisees. I try to be fair in all things and encourage all of our employees to be the best they can be. At the end of the day, we're a business, we are run like a business, and shareholders expect a return for their value invested as in any business." These comments flowed easily after the many 'dog and pony' shows Rebecca had led while promoting her IPO to the many potential institutional investors for the new stock. "I guess when it comes down to it, the real woman's touch is in the product."

"Well it sure is and I must say, the blueberry cheesecake crepe I had this morning with the cup of Costa Rican Blend was spectacular!"

"Thank you," replied Rebecca.

"One last question. While women are continuing to make progress toward equal pay for equal work, how have you balanced family responsibilities and work responsibilities? You're husband must be a saint!"

"Rick, my husband has been incredibly supportive of my career and dream for Cupcakes and Coffee. He often gets to his law job late after taking our two kids to school and has to leave early to pick the kids up if I am traveling, which I do over 50% of the time. He's truly been incredible and our children, well, we focus on quality time when I am in town and at home. It's the best we can do under the circumstances. The price for success is significant. Nothing is free."

Contemplating Rebecca's final comment, Robin repeated, "Nothing is free. Rebecca, it has been great to have you on Good Morning America and we wish you the best with Cupcakes and Coffee, the newest listing on the New York Stock Exchange, effective, well, yesterday morning. Congratulations!" Robin knew the interview was being taped.

Smiling and pleased, Rebecca responded, "Robin, it has been my pleasure and thank you for being such an inspiration to women around the world."

"Thank you."

A voice from the dark barked, "OK, cut! Are we good?"

After a brief pause, when it seemed like everyone in the studio sat on pins and needles, someone yelled, "We're good."

The set erupted into a mass of arms, legs, boom mics, cameras, chairs, and voices. Robin and Rebecca shook hands once again, exchanged pleasantries, and as fast as the interview had begun, it was over.

Mark appeared from the shadows, "That was great. You did really well."

"Well, thank you, but we'll see how it looks on TV tomorrow morning before passing final judgment. Thank you, though. Well, where to now?"

Unless you want to walk around New York all day looking like a pasty mannequin, let's get you back to make-up so they can get you looking normal and send you on your way. Your flight back to Kansas City leaves at 2:00 p.m. and in New York, especially LaGuardia, it's good to get to the airport at least two-and-a-half hours early in order to get through the security lines. We'll leave as soon as you are ready."

"Roger," offering a token salute, "As you wish, sir," Rebecca was still buzzing from the rush of the whole experience at ABC.

The Flight

"Now boarding Zones 2 and 3 for Flight 2073 to Kansas City," the speaker over the airport intercom chirped. Rebecca was already standing near the front of the group of anxious travelers as they began to shove toward the open gate door. She was thankful she traveled light with just a small brief case and small carry-on suit case.

Just because she made it through the open gate door, doesn't mean she made it onto the plane any sooner. The customers were queued up 20-deep at the door of the aircraft. Under her breath she whispered, "If I could only run my business like this . . ." The gentleman in front of her must have heard her, turned, and contributed, "Yeah, me, too. This is ridiculous."

After about five minutes of shuffling toward the open door of the jet,

Rebecca finally made it to the aisle at the center of the plane. She began to relax a bit. Almost there.

Softly she narrated, "22A . . . 22A . . . ahhhh." Placing her carry-on in the overhead compartment, Rebecca slid in and collapsed in her seat, thankful for the window seat for two reasons: she wouldn't have to rise and move for someone needing a chair to her inside and the window and interior aircraft skin would provide some support as a pillow. The adrenaline crash after the super high-rush of the day had caught up to her.

The speaker chirped, "Welcome to United Airlines . . .," she closed her eyes and was out.

"Ding. You may now turn on your electronic devices. While we expect a smooth flight, we ask that while you are seated, you keep your seatbelt fastened and pulled tight around your waist. We will update you on our estimated arrival time, once we get to our flying altitude of 33,000 feet."

Where am I, she thought, in the few seconds after the short, yet deep slumber. She checked the corners of her mouth for any evidence of saliva, a consequence of her deep nap. All was good. Shifting to sit upright, she glanced out the window and then to her right to see a young boy and a business man, perhaps the young man's father, in the aisle. She had a sense of relief knowing that she would not have to chat with her ad hoc neighbor on this flight. She wanted to think, reflect, and plan for her future and the future of Cupcakes and Coffee.

She stared out the window at the miniature landscape of Long Island as her mind began to work. The phrase 'nothing is free' kept bouncing around in her head. She remembered saying it and remembered Robin Roberts repeating it. There was no doubt she worked her tail off to get to where she and the company are today, but at what price? Okay, nothing is free, but at what price do we attain success? She made it personal. At what price have I attained success?

Am I too much like a man? Reflecting on her answers to the interview questions, it sure sounded like it. Robin had asked about any unique woman's touch at the company, and all I could identify was the product?! True, our product has a feminine touch. I do listen to our people and want the best for them, but don't most CEO's and most men? I would have to say, yes. So what is the difference, if any, at Cupcakes and Coffee? Her long stare out the window as she pondered these questions was interrupted by a flight attendant asking her if she would like a beverage.

"I'd like a tomato juice, please."

"Thank you," as the drink was passed without incident over the laps of her temporary neighbors. She grabbed it and sipped.

Her mind leapt to, so, what's next?

She thought to herself. Well now, I am no longer the sole owner of Cupcakes and Coffee. Thousands, if not tens-of-thousands of people now own shares of the company. They have invested their hard-earned savings in us, trusting us to be good stewards and return to them value for their investment. The butterflies began to rise. She took a big sip of her tomato juice. The tartness and cool journey of the juice down her throat made the acute stomach unrest better.

If I've learned anything, I've learned that business is all about serving customers well. Isn't that the purpose of business?! Without customers, what is a business? We've been really good at it! We just need to keep doing what we are doing; making great treats at a reasonable price and continuing to expand in the market. This won't be too bad . . . Rebecca tried to convince herself.

Who am I kidding? Nothing is easy. Nothing is free. The butterflies returned.

After a minute or two void of thoughts, she was able to gain some perspective, Hey, just enjoy the moment. It's not often a woman CEO gets to open the New York Stock Exchange trading day and be interviewed on GMA in the same day! I just became a multi-millionaire, I have a great husband; two great kids; if I want to exit the business, I can begin that transition and live a life of luxury with the wealth that was generated for me and my family today. What worries should I have?

The thought of her husband and children back in Atchison brought a calm to her that she hadn't felt all day. She shut her eyes envisioning their welcome as she exited her car. In under a minute, she was dozing in a restless slumber.

"Ding."

The volume of the speaker woke Rebecca up immediately.

"We are now beginning our final approach into Kansas City. Please turn off and stow away all electronic devices. Make sure your tray tables are returned to their full, upright, and locked position. Our flight attendants will be making one last pass through the cabin to collect any remaining trash. We hope you have enjoyed traveling with United Airlines today. We appreciate your business. If your future plans call for air travel, we hope you will choose United Airlines again. Welcome to Kansas City."

Welcome Home

The ride back to Atchison from the airport went quickly. It was now dusk in Kansas as the days were getting longer. The countryside between the airport and home was rolling and beautiful. Rebecca thought, it's good to be home.

Making the turn into her driveway, she saw a big banner stretched across her double-door garage. 'Congratulations and Welcome Home.' It reminded her of the welcome she received coming home after giving birth to Josh, their second child. She smiled.

At the sound of her car door shutting, her two children, Rick, and Cupcake, their dog, came pouring out of the front door. The children were running and screaming with Cupcake following along to see

11

what all the excitement was about. Rick was more measured in his welcome, but none-the-less happy to see his wife and celebrated CEO.

After settling in, transferring her dirty clothes to the laundry hamper, and changing into her favorite light fleece jogging suit, she sat down in the hearth room where her family was watching a kid's movie. Her children barely noticed her entry.

"Want something to drink?" asked Rick.

"Sure. Do we have any Chardonnay?"

"I think I can drum up a glass," rising as he pushed down the leg support on his recliner to execute the task for which he had just volunteered.

After sharing her experience of the day, Rick had the children kiss her goodnight and he marched them off to bed. Rebecca sat sipping her wine as the ten o'clock news began. She was curious if any of the local channels would sweep any of the news of her trading day opening. Her GMA interview would not air until tomorrow.

In the first five minutes of coverage, dominated by two homicides the previous night and a deadly accident on a rural two-lane road south of Kansas City, no coverage appeared of her big day on Wall Street.

Rick appeared and settled back into his recliner to join her watching the news.

"In national news today, the President signed into law two significant pieces of legislation that many conservatives fear will disrupt the still fragile economic recovery. Seen here signing HR Bill #3415, the Omnibus Employee Fairness and Livable Wage Act, the First Lady and presidents from numerous labor unions looked on and applauded the measure that had taken a congressional majority and two years of hard work to pass. People in the streets of Washington celebrated as over 75 million Americans just received a 15% pay raise; the first increase in the minimum wage in more than a decade."

"The other law signed by the President today also requires employers to participate in the payment of health insurance premiums for separated employees for up to 36 months post-employment. The minimum required participation is 30%."

"While labor unions and workers celebrated, there is wide-spread speculation that the market will open tomorrow with a significant correction on the heels of these late-afternoon legislative signings."

"In world news . . ."

After a few seconds of silence, Rebecca, set her jaw and commented, "This is enough to make me want to fold-up tent and go home. How is a business supposed to survive this? Most of our employees in our stores make more than minimum wage, but when the minimum wage adjusts, those who have worked for us for years and earned significant increases feel they deserve to have the same increase in their pay. That's simply a cost the business can't afford."

Rick sat and listened quietly.

"You know something, after that comment the President made months ago . . . something about an entrepreneur 'not doing it himself' – starting and growing a business – and this news, maybe I'll just resign tomorrow and make headlines that way. I can't believe this! What has happened to business in America? Our country is in big trouble." She swallowed the remaining quarter-glass of Chardonnay in one big swig.

"I'm going to bed."

The First Day Back

Rebecca's alarm music sounded.

Glancing at the clock, Rebecca switched the alarm off and shuffled to the bathroom. Though about to be featured on Good Morning America, her sleep had been restless and her mood was anything but joyous. The news last night had robbed her of the joy of the day.

Gathering her laptop and folders from her desk and packing her briefcase, Rebecca stopped to top off her travel mug with piping hot coffee before heading to the office. "Goodbye, guys! Love you!"

A muffled mix of, "Bye, have a good day, love you, bye," came from upstairs. She shut the front door.

At the office, now the headquarters of Cupcakes and Coffee, a publicly-traded company, her normal parking spot was available and she pulled into it, comfortable with the routine, but keenly aware that today was not likely to be business as usual.

She entered the foyer of the headquarters, a converted old warehouse in downtown Atchison, now housing all administrative functions of the company: research and development, IT, human resources, finance, franchise operations, and all executives. The building exterior was non-descript, wrapped in red brick. All the original warehouse windows had been replaced with thermal, double-pane, tinted windows, giving the building an entirely new, "I am not what you think," look.

The interior was anything but nondescript. Colorful would be an understatement, though not gaudy. All the furnishings were modern with antique brass and mocha-brown leather. The brass lighting fixtures matched the furniture. A wide array of colors, mixed on alternating walls and the ceiling, made the place feel happy and carefree. This was by design. Rebecca wanted the headquarters to mirror the feelings she wanted her customers to experience as they entered her stores.

Her outlook brightened immediately.

It was still early; at least an hour before most others would begin arriving at the office. She set her briefcase down to her left behind her desk, mounted her laptop on the docking station, and began to shuffle paper, envelopes, and folders on her desk, preparing to catch up from her New York trip. Before she knew it, people had been filing into the office and Brent, the Executive Vice President of Franchise Operations, stopped in her doorway.

"Good morning, Sunshine."

Glancing up, a bit startled by the voice that interrupted her reading an e-mail, "Good morning! What's going on this morning? Everything OK?"

"Yeah, yeah. Just checking in with you to see how the trip went."

"Oh, it was wonderful. The welcome at the Stock Exchange was great – wow, that's a huge place – I had no idea. I got to meet Robin Roberts!"

"Did she do your interview?"

"She sure did! What a wonderful woman."

"Well it had to be a great day for you." Brent followed with, "You've earned it. Congratulations."

"Thanks. And thanks to you and the rest of the team. I couldn't have done it without you."

They smiled at one another, both understanding that the exchange was over.

After an awkward silence, Brent remarked, "Hey, the team has assembled in the café to watch your interview on GMA this morning. Care to join us?"

Reluctantly, Rebecca acknowledged the expectation to join the team, as much as she didn't want to see herself on TV. "Sure, I'll be right down."

As she walked into the café, her team acknowledged her presence with a cheer and smattering of applause. Rebecca smiled and said, "Thank you," as she navigated to the coffee station for a fresh cup of her favorite snickerdoodle-flavored coffee.

Brent prompted her, "Well, do you have anything to say before we see you on TV?"

Rebecca turned toward her team, now numbering over 100 in the cafe. She looked down into the rich mocha color of her flavored coffee and spoke. "Well first of all, thank you for the warm welcome. I really appreciate it. You all have been great to me and to the company. I can't thank you enough. We've had a great ride, but today is a new day with heightened expectations. The stock of the company is now publicly-traded. That means that we have thousands of people who have invested in our stock who expect to receive a return on their money. Your allegiance must be to them." Correcting herself, "Our allegiance must now be to them."

She paused taking a sip of coffee.

"There will be much more to come over the next few weeks about what that means. In the meantime, enjoy the increased attention on our company." She regretted using the word 'enjoy' as she wasn't sure she could do what she had just asked her employees to do.

Someone shouted, "Hey, the interview is about to start." Everyone turned to one of two large flat screens in the café just in time to hear George Stephanopolous introduce Robin Roberts and an interview taped yesterday with 'one of the most-respected female CEO's in the country.' That comment drew a smattering of gratuitous applause from her team.

Robin Roberts began her interview, "Good morning, America. It is my pleasure to introduce . . ." Rebecca's taped interview aired.

Applause erupted in the café as ABC cut back to George at the anchor desk when the interview ended.

Many turned toward Rebecca to witness her reaction. A simple shrug of the shoulders said it all. No big deal – though she knew deep down that it was a very big deal. Employees began to head back to their offices and cubicles to continue their work for the day, while a few employees stopped to personally congratulate Rebecca before doing so.

In five minutes, she was alone with her thoughts in the café. I do love this place, she thought to herself. She topped off her coffee and headed back to her office to continue her work, just as others had obediently done.

Part II

The First Lunch

Her morning flew by. After answering e-mails, returning a few calls, and speaking to someone from the Kansas City Star who saw the interview and wanted a comment, she briskly walked past her Assistant, Carrie, and said as she walked, "I'm headed over to Jerry's Again for lunch. I should be back by 1:00 or so."

"OK, have a nice lunch." Rebecca was in the elevator and gone.

The three block walk to Jerry's Again was nice. The temperature was in the high 60's, with low humidity . . . a perfect mid-spring day. Jerry's Again was located on a corner in downtown Atchison. The lighting was soft, the menu narrow, and the service impeccable.

It was a favorite lunch destination for many town folk and the hundreds of visitors who bussed daily from Kansas City and the region to visit the biggest retail attraction in Atchison; Nell Hills, a home interior décor and inspiration retail store. With all consciousness, Rebecca had opened her first Cupcakes and Coffee store adjacent to Nell Hills to capitalize on the regular visiting foot traffic. It had proven to be a brilliant move.

"Good morning, err, afternoon Liz," glancing at her watch to make sure her greeting was accurate. It was 12:01.

"Good morning, Rebecca. Great to see you! Congratulations on your interview. I watched it before coming to the restaurant this morning.

When I get time, I'd love to hear about your experience. Did you get to meet Josh?"

"No, I didn't meet Josh, but just let me know when and I'd be glad to share it with you." Rebecca sat in a corner booth for two, hoping and expecting to be alone for lunch.

After studying the already-very-familiar menu, Rebecca ordered a chicken Caesar salad with an unsweetened iced tea. She folded the menu and returned it to the server, unwrapped her utensils and placed the cloth napkin in her lap. She glanced up to see who else was in the restaurant. It looked like the normal crowd; a few business people, some lawyers, a team of road workers in their reflective vests, and a monk sitting alone.

She watched the midday news silently as they covered the same news that was covered that morning. Typical, she quipped to herself. Way too much of the same news coverage.

"In business news, the stock market fell over 500 points this morning on the news of the legislation signed by the President last night that mandates a minimum wage increase of 15% effective in three months and employer participation in paying health insurance premiums for separated employees for up to 36 months. Reaction from the business and investment community has been harsh and the free fall of stock prices this morning evidences their dissatisfaction."

"In other news . . ."

Well, well, well, she thought to herself. I'm not the only one disgusted with the happenings in Washington.

"Excuse me."

Startled by the voice, she promptly chewed and swallowed her latest fork-full of salad to turn and see the monk who had been sitting alone across the room.

"Yes, how may I help you?" asked Rebecca as she carefully manicured the corners of her mouth with her cloth napkin.

"Are you Rebecca Morton?"

"Yes, I am," asking again, "How may I help you?"

My name is Brother Mark. I am a monk at the Abbey on campus here in town."

Extending her hand to shake his, Rebecca responded, "Very nice to meet you, I am Rebecca."

"It's my pleasure. I just wanted to say that I enjoyed watching your interview this morning on Good Morning America with Robin Roberts. You did a nice job."

Embarrassed, yet appreciative, she offered a warm, "Thank you."

"If you don't mind, may I ask you a few questions?"

Rebecca nodded.

"I've watched your company grow and expand over the last few years, and it's amazing what you have accomplished."

"Thank you," now sounding like a scratched record she thought. "Please sit down." She moved her water and tea glass closer to her plate to create more of a shared space at the small table, battling her desire to be alone, yet succumbing to her desire to be hospitable and accommodating. "So, what would you like to know?"

"It must have been a whirlwind to grow your company as fast as you have and still maintain quality, not to mention cohesiveness and cooperation. How did you accomplish that?"

"Pardon me," taking a small sip of tea, "but I am a little shocked that a monk is asking me intimate questions about my business. I mean, you're a monk, right? You live a meditative, if not cloistered life in a monastic community, dedicated to worshipping and honoring God."

"That's somewhat accurate, but that's not all the life we lead. We do much more."

"I am sorry to turn the tables on you, but what you said sounds a lot more interesting than what I have to offer you. What more to your life is there?"

Brother Mark settled into his seat and shared, "I was not always a monk. I have never been married and have always felt close to God and the monks at this Abbey. It all started when I was in college here. But I also felt called to the world of commerce and business. Upon graduation, I spent 15-years in the healthcare industry, serving a group of hospitals as a manager and executive. I returned to get my MBA about five-years in and just completed my PhD a couple of years ago in business leadership. About four years ago, I chose to return to join the monks in the Abbey.

"Wow, I would have never guessed . . . I mean with the black robe and all. To tell you the truth, the black robes and hoods kind of creep me out."

"I understand and no offense taken. Given my journey, I have a love for God and a passion to see business do the good things for which God intended."

This comment surprised Rebecca. "Hmmm," she responded respectfully yet doubtful of the truth in it.

"You seem to doubt this."

"Well, I've never heard that, and to use God and business in the same sentence sounds odd. They seem so contrary to me. God is soft and loving. Business is hard and harsh."

"I understand. It all sounded odd to me, too, when I first heard it, but the more I studied the idea and researched the thought, and put what I learned into practice, the more I saw the truth in it."

"Very interesting . . ."

Brother Mark continued, "What do you think of the stock market crash today? Pretty scary, isn't it?"

"Oh yes. It's horrible . . . not the market decline itself, but the legislation passed yesterday that caused the crash. It's a really sad day for business." Rebecca glanced up at the small TV in the corner to see if there were any updates on the scrolling feeds across the bottom of the screen.

"Look! The market loss is now in record territory – over 800 points." Rebecca shook her head in disgust.

Brother Mark turned to look and shook his head to affirm her observation. "Wow, it's a bad day for a lot of people. But it must be a pretty good day for you," swinging back to face Rebecca, "A new IPO, opening up the trading day yesterday, fresh off a GMA interview this morning . . ."

"You'd think so, wouldn't you? But I don't know. I'm not ready to acknowledge how I feel right now about it all, but the future scares me. If Congress can pass legislation like that which passed yesterday, and the stock market can lose 800 points by midday, I'm not sure how excited I can be about anything in business." She pushed her plate away, done with her meal and lifted her glass for a final gulp or two of tea.

"Well, keep everything in perspective. You've been blessed with so much and I celebrate that with you. To whom much is given, much will be required.[5] It was a pleasure meeting you." Brother Mark slid a business card across the table for Rebecca. "I hope our paths

---

5 The Holy Bible, Luke 12:48 (ESV)

cross again. Congratulations on your success." With a smile and handshake, he turned and left the restaurant.

Rebecca located the meal check on the table and dug twelve dollars out of her purse for the lunch and tip. Waiving to Liz and wishing her a good afternoon, Rebecca returned to her office, reversing the travel path by which she had come.

Sitting heavily into her office chair, content from a good, healthy midday meal, and taking a deep breath, she removed Brother Mark's card from her purse. Looking at it, she couldn't believe what she saw. The name read Brother Mark Sculley, Executive Consultant, with the Abbey name and address. It was the subtitle under his name that struck her. Nothing is free. And she didn't think this was an intentional reference to his billing rate.

Supper Time

Rebecca's afternoon was filled with executive meetings about the changes and expectations to come. Summer cupcake and crepe tasting sessions from the R&D kitchen took about an hour. Those were always fun and filling meetings! Updates on the progress of the two newest stores opening in California this month took another 45 minutes. Review of the mid-month financial statements took 30-minutes. Had she been able to anticipate and think ahead, she would not have ended her day with meetings about the pending law changes. The effect on the business will be substantial and the work to comply with the requirements will cost hundreds of thousands of dollars in legal fees and direct work to alter company policies.

At 5:30 p.m. they adjourned their last meeting. Everyone left depressed and demoralized.

It was a quiet, yet short ride home.

A deep breath after stepping inside the house told Rebecca that garlic bread was in the oven. When Annie and Josh heard the front door close, they ran from wherever they were to greet their Mom.

"Mommy! Mommy's home!" They hugged her until they could hug no more, and just as quickly as the hugs began, they were over. Off they went to continue the growth of their imagination watching something that Rebecca hoped was healthy.

"Hello, Honey," said Rick as he pecked her on the cheek.

"Your famous lasagna tonight?"

"How did you know?" Rick knew full well the normal aroma in the house when lasagna was being served.

Rebecca smiled and headed upstairs to get comfortable.

At the dining room table – unlike most families, the Morton's actually used their formal table for their family meals; not just holiday meals – Rick and Rebecca sat across from one another and the children did likewise. The entire meal was set before them; a salad already chopped and tossed in vinaigrette dressing, a pan of baked lasagna, and a basket of hot, buttered and sliced garlic bread. Rick had taken the extra step to pour glasses of Chianti for himself and his celebrated CEO wife.

"This looks awesome," commented Rebecca, breathing deeply and smiling at everyone around the table. They dug in.

Nothing but silverware on porcelain could be heard for a good five minutes.

"Mommy, can I go now?" asked Josh.

Rick intervened before Rebecca could answer and said, "Take two more bites of your lasagna, then you can go." Josh looked disappointed but did as he was told.

"Now?" giving Rick the puppy-dog-eye treatment. Rebecca was humored watching this like she imagined a ghost might watch a human activity – present, but invisible.

25

"Yes." Josh scrambled from the table.

"Me, too?"

"Yes, Annie, you can go, too."

Rick and Rebecca sat grazing on what remained on their plates. Rick poured another two glasses of wine. Both were well satisfied with the delicious home-cooked meal.

Rebecca began the conversation, "So, how was your day?"

"Same old, same old," said Rick. "One deposition, two trial appearances – short as they may have been, one settlement, and a little research for tomorrow. Nothing special . . . just trying to do my part to keep the streets of our hometown free from riff-raff."

Rebecca smiled at Rick's feeble attempt at humor.

Rick reciprocated, "How about yours?"

"Overall, it was a good day, I guess. The team forced me to watch my GMA interview with them in the cafeteria. They said some nice things. Did I look fat on TV to you?" Rebecca had heard that's what happens on TV.

"No, you looked great," being totally honest with her.

Rebecca took a sip of wine and continued, "I had the strangest experience at lunch today. I was seated in my normal corner booth eating my salad when this monk from the Abbey comes over and introduces himself."

"Really?!"

"Yeah. He said his name was Brother Mark. He said he had watched my GMA interview and asked if he could ask me a few questions. So I said sure. He was very nice and polite."

To use God and business in the same sentence sounds odd.

Inquisitively, Rick followed, "So what did he ask about?"

"Well, he asked about how I was able to lead such a quick growth effort and not lose control or favor with our team and customers."

"Wow, that's a pretty good question coming from a clergyman."

"I know! It was weird, so I asked him how a monk has this level of interest in a business . . . in my business?"

Rick leaned in with both elbows on the table and his wine glass between his hands.

"He shared a bit of his history. He was unmarried, but had been a manager and executive at numerous hospitals. Because he said he loved God, he wanted to return and join the monks at the Abbey. He added that he had a passion to see business do the good things God wanted it to do, or something like that." Rebecca sipped.

Rick sat back in his chair. "What a strange comment. I can't say I've ever heard that God wants business to do good; especially coming from a man of the cloth; especially one associated with a college! Those are the most liberal thinking group of leftists on the planet. Business doing good?!" Sarcasm was front and center.

After a brief silence, Rick added, "I tell you, his comment shows some real insight." Rick sipped his wine.

Rebecca pondered. I think business does good. Look at the jobs Cupcakes and Coffee has generated in Atchison and around the country. Almost 200 here, and 6,000 plus in total! We have served delicious food to millions of customers for which we exchange value for currency. God knows, you and I pay our share of taxes. The combined total of taxes paid by employees of Cupcakes and Coffee must be near $30 million. Business does good, more confident now in her thinking.

Rick noticed her face tweaking as she pondered, as if she were having her own internal conversation. "What are you thinking?"

"Oh, I don't know. Business does do good, doesn't it? Then why do so many people – what did you call them – the 'liberal group of leftists' – think business is bad?"

Letting that question hang rhetorically, as if on cue, Rick and Rebecca rose simultaneously and began clearing the dishes and tableware from the dining room.

The evening before bed was like any other evening. Prime time TV watching with Annie and Josh upstairs doing what young kids do; some nominal laughter; a few trips to the fridge for a bottled water and ice cream.

Rick 'did the duty' again of getting the kids ready for bed as Rebecca grabbed a night cap of Bailey's on-the-rocks.

Before the news started, Rebecca battened down the house, picked up the stray glasses and bowls, turned off the lights and went upstairs to kiss the kids goodnight.

She and Rick met in bed just as the opening local breaking news had ended with a commercial.

"Thanks for dinner tonight. It was delicious." She leaned over and pecked him on the cheek.

"You're welcome."

They sat silently as the two minutes of commercials drug on.

The news anchor desk appeared, "In business news today, the stock market fell a record 1,017 points to close at 12,158 on the heels of the legislation signed into law yesterday by the President. Market analysts predict another bad day for investors as confidence in the environment for business is waning. Experts fear inflation on the horizon with an increase in overall costs of American-made products and the related decrease in U.S. exports. This comes at a time when the economic recovery, fragile as it is, was beginning to make confident strides."

Scenes of the New York Stock Exchange trading floor with order tickets all over the floor and depressed traders milling around with looks of worry on their faces provided the backdrop for the story.

"In other news . . ."

Rebecca sighed. "I wonder what happened to our share price today? I'm not used to having to look at it or worry about it." She confessed, "I don't want to know any bad news before I go to bed, though. Are you ready?" wanting to turn off the TV.

Rick, with his eyes already shut, issued an unintelligible, "Uh huh."

Rebecca turned off the TV and the bedside light. Her thoughts bounced between the details of work for tomorrow and the worry she felt about her business. In a few minutes, she began a bout of restless sleep.

The Second Day Back

Morning brought a respite from the torment of a variety of bad dreams, only remnants of which Rebecca could remember. A warm shower, and a full travel mug of coffee, made the day feel just like any other day. It was another bright, mid-spring morning.

On the way to the office, she decided to stop by the original Cupcakes and Coffee store adjacent to Nell Hills, just to check in. Marj, the long-time store manager, had been a fixture in the store since its beginning; starting as a server and cashier and moving up to manager quickly. She was bright, very customer-focused, and highly competent. Every year she ranked in the top echelon of Cupcakes and Coffee store managers around the country.

The glass door chimed, signaling the entry of another customer into the store as Rebecca entered.

Without looking up, an employee remarked, "Welcome to Cupcakes and Coffee, we'll be right with you."

Remembering the United Airlines script, . . . 'return your tray tables to their full, upright, and locked position,' she was pleased that the training scripts taught to her employees were still in place and practiced. She never got tired of being warmly welcomed into a store.

The store smelled delicious. The aroma of medium-roast coffee was warm and inviting. This had been a very conscious decision as Rebecca thought the Starbucks stores in the area smelled like skunk with the residual aroma of dark-roast coffee.

There were three people ahead of her in line. Each was treated very well by the order taker/cashier while the gentleman, Rebecca had forgotten his name, prepared the requested food to order on the back counter. The process was smooth, without obstacle, and got each customer on his or her way in about a minute. That was their target metric for customer turnover from order to delivery. They had experienced some problems with queuing in the past, so each store was now equipped with two registers; the second to be used when the line exceeded six people. At least that was the policy.

It was now Rebecca's turn to order.

"Good morning. How may I . . . Whoa! You surprised me. Hello, Rebecca!

Glancing at the employee's name badge, Rebecca replied, "Good morning, Shauna. How are you?"

"Great! Thanks."

"Are you here for a 'goody' or just here to observe or talk with Marj?"

"I wanted to stop by and say hello and see how things are going. How are they?"

Having done this before and knowing the expectations, Shauna hit a few keys on the cash register and reported to Rebecca, "We have served 25 customers already today for total sales revenue of $154.32 and an average ticket of $6.17."

"Not bad. Nice work. Is Marj in the back?"

"Yes, she is. Hey, Paul, would you please let Marj know that Rebecca is here to see her."

"Sure."

Rebecca interrupted, "Oh, that's OK. I'll just head back myself."

"You're the boss!"

Rebecca headed back. The door chimed again. "Welcome to Cupcakes and Coffee. How may I help you?" She smiled to herself.

Marj was busy preparing her daily order form, comparing the perpetual inventory quantities to forecast demand for the next five days.

"Good morning, Marj."

"Well, lookie who's here! Marj rose and embraced Rebecca, their normal method of greeting one another. Standing back and looking Rebecca from head-to-toe, "You're looking good."

"You, too," returning the compliment to Marj.

Marj, in common Cupcakes and Coffee protocol, asked, "How may I help you?"

"I was just checking in on my favorite store manager to see how things are going in the trenches. Your team did a nice job out front and your sales today are pretty good so far."

"Yeah, we've had a good week, year-on-year. The customers are loyal and they really like some of the new innovative crepes and cakes."

"That's good to hear!"

Finished with the pleasantries and shallow exchanges, Rebecca lowered her gaze, equally distributed her weight on both feet, and asked, "So, what are you hearing and thinking about two things: one being the IPO, and the other being the new laws just passed?"

Marj, pulled a chair out and insisted, "Please, take a seat." Once Rebecca was seated, Marj looked toward the door to ensure no one was within an earshot of her.

She began, "The IPO is exciting for many of us, but also scary. We've all heard what happens to privately-owned companies when they suddenly have the pressure of external investors; the quarterly earnings targets and the short-term decisions made at the expense of long-term results. That scares me!"

Rebecca nods her affirmation and understanding.

Marj checks the hallway again, leans in and begins to whisper, "Both Shauna and Paul asked about their raise this morning when they came in. I asked them, 'What raise?' They said that with the minimum wage going up they hinted at an equivalent increase in their pay. I told them I'd have to check on that. So I guess I'll ask you about any such raise."

Rebecca slid back in her chair and sighed, "I knew this was coming. I am not sure how I am going to handle this, but it is an issue. Can you tell them we are working on it and will respond shortly?"

"Ok. Rebecca, the part that really scares me is the post-employment health insurance. How will the company survive that? I understand the need, but can any company survive that?"

Rebecca sat upright, "I don't know, but it's going to be very difficult to maintain our margins without increasing prices to customers which could be disastrous." She sat back in her chair again.

They both looked at each other for a few seconds, understanding that they were in this together.

"We have a lot of work to do, don't we?" remarked Rebecca. "And we have a whole bunch of new shareholders who expect great things." Butterflies began to rise in her stomach. She smiled through the unrest.

"Well, I'll let you get back to work. Thank you for sharing your thoughts with me. I always appreciate your perspective."

"Thanks for coming by the store. We miss you when we don't see you. Will you tell me about your GMA interview sometime? That had to be awesome! Did you meet Josh?"

"No, I didn't meet Josh, and, yes, I will when we have more time. Thanks again," extending both arms for a hug. "We'll see you later. Tell your team they are doing a great job."

"Sure will. Bye now." Rebecca left through the hallway and headed to her office. She was worried.

The New Laws

Setting her briefcase down to her left, she began her morning routine of cleaning-up, reading e-mails and returning phone calls. She felt hurried because of what Marj had shared.

As soon as the nominal work was done, she put in a call to Brent, the Executive VP of Franchise Operations. He picked-up after the first ring.

"Hello, Rebecca. How may I help you?"

"Brent, good morning. I stopped by Store #1 today, just to check in on things.

Brent shifted his weight in his chair expecting that she saw something she didn't like.

"Marj shared with me that her two day shift employees had asked about their expected raise. When asked, they said, because the minimum wage went up, they expected to get an equivalent increase. I anticipated this reaction from some. Now I need to know how prevalent this mindset is throughout the company. Would you please blast out a survey to all our franchise store managers and find out how prevalent this perspective is."

Mark relaxed a bit, realizing her call was not related to a performance issue. "Sure, I'll get one out this morning."

"Oh, and please be careful how you ask the question. I don't want to create an issue where one doesn't exist. Does that make sense?"

"Perfectly. I'll get right on it."

"Thank you. Goodbye."

Rebecca, though tense, began to feel a little better that progress of some sort was being made. She resigned herself to patience waiting for the results of the survey to come back. That was not easy for a 'get it done' type CEO. Patience was not her strong suit.

In the 'busyness' of the morning, a sudden thought hit her. I haven't checked our stock price on the market today!

She immediately began banging on the keys on her laptop to pull-up the New York Stock Exchange. She entered the trading symbol for Cupcakes and Coffee – CUPC – and waited for the refreshed page.

Anticipating a price near $15 per share, the IPO price, she waited, impatiently, of course.

With a few blinks and grunts of her laptop, the screen finally arrived in the form of a price graph. The timeline on the x-Axis was short, given that the stock had only traded for three days. The values on the y-Axis ranged from $0.00 to $20.00. Because of the small window on the x-Axis she had to zoom in to discern the trend line. It looked at first like one vertical line from about $10.00 to $15.00.

She clicked on the zoom icon, and gasped as what she saw.

The stock for Cupcakes and Coffee, which opened at the IPO ask price of $15.00 per share had risen to $16.52 during its initial offering day and then had plummeted to $13.12 on day two, and was now trading at $11.96.

She felt sick. She had to turn away from the screen.

The butterflies swooned. She put her head down, with her eyes resting on the inside pillows of her hands. She rubbed gently, careful not to smear her make-up whispering, "What do I do?"

Her worrisome meditation was broken by the beep of the intercom on her phone.

"Rebecca?" Carrie queried, "You have a call from a Mr. Anderson at Fidelity Investment Advisors on line two."

Rebecca shot up and hesitated in her response, "Uhhh, Ok. Please tell Mr. Anderson that I am tied up at the moment and that I will return his call."

"Will do. Thank you."

Rebecca pushed the Intercom button off and set her phone to Do Not Disturb.

Now she could be alone with her thoughts. Her experience informed her that when trouble was brewing, it was best to isolate and begin the deep thinking process. It had produced significant results in the past. So she did exactly that.

An hour of quiet, contemplative pacing around her office had yielded some results. Her mind sequenced her findings:

- The fact is the entire stock market has crashed.

- Our stock price will likely often mirror the market, especially in times of trouble like this. (Deep down, she hoped for the same in times of prosperity)

- Our plan, our investments, our people, and our product haven't changed.

- I haven't changed! I don't know whether that is good or bad.

- The government and administration catalyzed this problem with the passing of legislation that increases the cost of doing business.

All of this made perfect sense to her, and because it did, she had calmed down. A couple of big questions still remained, though:

What do I say to any investors or fund managers who call about our stock's performance? They can't be happy.

What do I do at the company about issues raised by the passing of this legislation to mitigate the pain and damage, while giving us the best chance of success?

She thought again. No, in this case, it's about survival, not just success.

Rebecca glanced at her watch. It was 11:50 am. The morning had disappeared. Gathering her purse quickly, her mind still wrapped around the intense thoughts of the morning, she headed for the elevator, giving a quick, "Going to lunch," verbal tweet to Carrie on the way out.

The Second Lunch

Jerry's Again was bustling today, though she was not worried about her table-for-two being available. This time, she hoped that one Brother Mark had decided to sample the lunch fare at about the same time again today.

Craning her neck to look through the crowd waiting to be seated, she scanned right, then left, looking for an all-black outfit that might indicate the presence of Brother Mark.

There! In the center-back was who she had hoped to see.

She thought to herself, there must be a God. I can't believe he is here and that he is alone.

Politely, but with determination, she made her way to the hostess podium and asked if she could join 'the gentlemen at the table over there,' pointing in the direction of Brother Mark. The hostess obliged, and escorted her to his table.

His table was just under one of the big flat screens in the restaurant. The TV was tuned to Bloomberg and a talking head was saying something about the stock market, though the volume was muted. A ticker-tape scrolled right-to-left at the bottom of the screen displaying red down-arrow after red down-arrow beside the stock trading symbols.

"Good morning," offered Rebecca, glancing at her watch to confirm the proper greeting, "Yes, good morning."

Brother Mark rose as a courtesy, not yet knowing to whom he owed the pleasure of this encounter, as he had been in the middle of gathering a fork full of salad. "Well, hello! Good morning to you Ms. Rebecca – trusting she had been right about the time of day. How are you?"

"I am fine, thank you," extending her hand to complete the greeting in a professional manner.

Normally, Rebecca would expect the common and institutionalized follow-up phrase, "How may I help you," so ingrained at Cupcakes and Coffee, but after a few awkward seconds, she resigned herself that it wasn't coming. Not everyone thought like her.

Not wanting to be forward, nor too revealing at this point. She moved her head in the direction of the TV above them, then looked at it, "I see you're watching the financial Armageddon this fine day."

"Yes, yes. I have always been fascinated with how the stock market works and it's interesting to me to consider how all the corporate CEO's are handling this, as you say, 'Armageddon.' I imagine many are scrambling for answers that just won't come." Still standing and recognizing his lack of hospitality, "Please, Rebecca, have a seat. No need to stand there all lunch."

They both settled into their seats. Rebecca was thankful her back was to the TV. She didn't want to be distracted.

"May I treat you to lunch today?" asked Brother Mark.

"Thank you for allowing me to sit with you, but I must treat you to lunch."

"And why might that be?"

"Because I need to ask you a few questions, if you don't mind. Feel free to bill me at your normal consulting hourly rate," recalling the subtitle on his business card.

Brother Mark smiled. "No need for that. I work for food."

This made Rebecca laugh; the first time in a couple of days.

The server took Rebecca's beverage order, and as is often appropriate in a business setting, she ordered the same meal that Brother Mark was having; a Chef salad, though she opted for vinaigrette dressing on the side instead of ranch.

"So, how may I help you," came the all-to-familiar phrase from Brother Mark's mouth. She knew what to do now.

Rebecca began, "Well, you've been watching the devastation in the stock market, at least while you've been sitting here." Brother Mark affirmed with a shake of his head as he chewed a bite of salad. "Our stock has followed the market down and is now trading at about 20% less than where it opened three days ago. I am worried and frustrated."

He swallowed his latest bite and sipped his water, Brother Mark commented, "I certainly understand," yet he offered no advice. His pause invited her to continue.

"Here is my first question. I am beginning to have investors and investment managers call me. I imagine they want a report about our stock price and what the company is doing to bolster it. I have no experience with this and would like your advice and counsel. What do I do?"

Brother Mark cleared his throat. "First of all, know you are not alone in this. You can bet CEO's all over the country and world are fielding calls like this, trying to breed confidence in the investment community for their stock to stop the selling free-fall."

This reality did make Rebecca feel a little better.

"Secondly, you should be proactive when anything like this happens. Don't wait for investors to call the company. Issue a press release aimed at convincing the investing public that your strategy, your planned investments, your talented people, and your value proposition haven't changed."

This sounded eerily familiar.

"Do you have an investor relations specialist at the company?"

Rebecca responded, "We have a Public Relations Manager, but no one specifically assigned to investor relations."

"That would be a good place to start," advised Brother Mark.

Rebecca nodded her understanding.

The server delivered Rebecca's salad and dressing. Rebecca began pouring her dressing over the colorful mix of vegetables and meats.

"The stock market is an interesting beast, isn't it," prompted Brother Mark.

"That's an odd choice of words," challenged Rebecca as she took a bite of salad.

"It is, but it's not without merit," the monk sparred back.

Rebecca swallowed the bite, waiting for more.

"The stock market is a wonderful tool on which investors can trade their investments in companies just like you trade cupcakes for currency. If someone values a stock for more than it is currently worth, they can buy it from another investor who is interested in selling it. You sell a cupcake when a customer values the cupcake at or more than the price at which you are selling it."

Rebecca thought to herself, that is simple enough. The simplicity and clarity were soothing.

"That's all it is, though – a market. Unfortunately, the uninformed have attributed way too much meaning and weight to its measure and its related fluctuations."

Holding her iced tea in both hands, Rebecca said, "Tell me more."

"Well, in any unimpeded market, prices fluctuate based upon numerous variables; the available supply, demand against that supply, and both real and perceived value. When a catalyst, like that which happened earlier this week with the laws passed is experienced by the demand variable or buyers for stock, demand drops precipitously. There is a glut of supply in the market. Prices fall. In addition, the perceived value of an investment also declines."

"I understand the economic theory behind supply and demand in an unimpeded market, but tell me more about why perceived value declines." Rebecca continued to eat her salad at a leisurely pace.

Brother Mark continued with a question, "How do you think stocks are valued in the market?"

Rebecca finished her sip of tea and responded, "I would imagine stock prices have some correlation to the return expected by the investor."

"Correct, but there is an important factor here that is not factual. It is forecast. Investors don't usually buy an investment for a singular annual return. They invest for a period of time during which either anticipated dividends are returned to them in the form of cash, or company earnings and cash flows grow generating potential or perceived future value for the stock. In this way, their investment is speculative in nature. No return is guaranteed. The risk of investing in forecasted earnings and cash flows can generate significant returns, if they come to fruition."

"I get that."

"When the audience of buyers learns of things that could damage those future earnings and cash flows, many sell their investment in order to minimize any future losses. The loss is not real yet, but the perceived future value of their investment has taken a hit, so perceived value plays into the pricing equation."

Rebecca set her glass down. "So, in our situation, our investors bought Cupcakes and Coffee stock at a price based upon both the real and perceived future value of our earnings and cash flows. These forecasts, though unscientific, are based upon our strategies and future plans, reinforced by our past performance, which has been very good."

"Yes," replied Brother Mark.

"Independent of our activities, a negative catalyst was introduced into the market, and because the expectation is that these laws will likely increase costs, shrink margins, and possibly hurt demand for our product, the future perceived value of an investment in our stock went down."

"Exactly."

Rebecca leaned back in her chair, now more satisfied with the explanation for the fall in her company's stock price. "But what about the stock market being a beast? I don't get that."

"There is something bigger going on here. Absent other periodic and meaningful metrics of company performance, since companies only periodically report financial results and privately-held companies rarely do, as you know, speculative investors make investment decisions on the information they do have. On a side note, this is why insider information is so valuable to speculative investors. This is why some people are willing to risk their lives and livelihoods by illegally trading stocks on insider information. The legal information they do have is represented best live and in-color in pricing on the stock market. Any little bit of positive news or negative news can start either a market swell or a market slide. The stock market trades on information, not on real value created."

Rebecca affirmed her understanding with a headshake.

"The beast reference relates to the weight and truth attributed to the market as it relates to both the U.S. and global economy. Have you noticed that when media outlets report on the U.S. economy, they most often quote the Dow Jones Industrial Index, the Standard and Poor's

Index, or the overall gain or loss on the New York Stock Exchange or NASDAQ for the day?"

"Yes, daily reports on the economy frequently start there."

"The association drawn by the media between the stock market and the U.S. economy, which is measured more by real investment, real employment, and real value created, generates numerous urgent short-term responses; responses we would have if we were being chased by something or someone who could hurt us; a beast as it were. It would dominate our thoughts and control our behavior, much like the stock market controls business today."

"I think I get it."

"You see, the market crash in 2008 was less a financial crisis, than it evidences an anthropological or cultural crisis. We tend to attribute our entire economy to the rise and fall of the stock market. That's a very dangerous beast."

Rebecca thought as she responded, "I can see how we do that."

"Do you remember what happened a few months ago when an erroneous tweet about a bomb in or near the White House caused the stock market to lose 2% of its value in minutes?"

"Yes. I remember hearing something about that on the news."

"The market trades on information; some good and some bad, some accurate, some inaccurate. Yet we widely attribute our entire economy to its whims. That's why it's a beast. That's why we have a cultural crisis. Business is so much more than the stock market. There is so much more good God intended for business to do."[6]

---

6 Pontifical Council for Justice and Peace, with the John A. Ryan Institute for Catholic Social Thought at the University of St. Thomas, Minnesota, USA, *The Vocation of the Business Leader – A Reflection*, 3e, 41. "The business leader is not a speculator, but essentially an innovator. The speculator makes it his goal to maximize profit; for him, business is merely a means to an end, and that end is profit. [...] It should be immediately clear that the speculator is not the model of business leader which the Church holds up as an agent and builder of the common good."

There it was again. God and business. This time Rebecca recognized the comment, but it did not generate the same doubt. Rebecca smiled.

"Wow. I should buy you lunch and dinner for all that!"

"No need. I hope what I shared with you makes sense. My experience and my studies tell me this is true. I know it's getting late, but I'd like to leave you with something to ponder."

Curious, Rebecca said, "OK?"

The stock market trades on information, not on real value created.

"If the stock market is only thinly correlated to real economic growth or decline, then why do business leaders continue to harness their wagons to the idea that the purpose of business is to maximize shareholder wealth?" Brother Mark leaned in and raised his eyebrows in a show of mutual intellectual curiosity.

Placing her napkin on her empty plate, Rebecca responded, "I'll have to think about that one."

Rebecca waived the server over for the check, gave her a $50 dollar bill, and waited for the change and return receipt.

"Thank you for allowing me to join you for lunch today."

"It was my pleasure," as Brother Mark rose to depart. "I hope your afternoon is better. Know you are blessed."

Rebecca gratuitously acknowledged his comments with a shake of his hand. "Thank you. I hope so, too. I hope to continue our discussions."

"Me, too. Good bye." Brother Mark left and Rebecca counted out a 20% tip, plus some, gathered her purse, and headed back to the office.

Afternoon Adjustments

Not unexpected, her desk was just as she left it, with the exception of the fish tank screen saver generating bubbles on her lap top, and a stack of phone message forms with Mr. Anderson's from Fidelity Investment Advisors on top. Rebecca settled in for the afternoon.

Brother Mark's first piece of advice at lunch was number one on her priority list.

"Carrie, please get me Kyle. I'd like to meet with him immediately. Thank you."

After a few minutes, Rebecca heard a knock on her door. "Come in."

Kyle Masterson entered. "Good afternoon, Rebecca, how may I help you?"

"Kyle, thanks for coming up on such short notice." Rebecca moved around her desk and motioned to the small conference table in her office. On the table was a lone dish of butter mints. "Please sit down."

"Kyle, now that our stock is publicly-traded, we need to focus some of our public relations resources on investor relations. I have no experience in the investor relations arena, but I know your public relations expertise is core to the function and work. An executive mentor of mine (she was thinking of Brother Mark) advised me that this role is a top priority."

Kyle was writing notes as Rebecca spoke.

"I have had a couple of calls today from investors. I have chosen not speak to them until I was ready. The calls are indicative of the pressure and concern felt by investors during this stock market slide. Have you seen our share price today?"

Kyle stopped writing. "No, I haven't."

"It's not good. Kyle, part of your role every day until further notice is to check the stock price three-times a day, throughout the day." Kyle looked confused, since his expertise was communication with people, not financial metrics.

"We need to communicate proactively with our investors about what we are doing to overcome the stock price decline. I am assuming that even in times of prosperity, we should be proactive to communicate the things we are doing well and intend on continuing to reinforce the stock value. We must not take our shareholders for granted. Is this clear?"

Kyle felt better understanding now that this role was about communication and very much within his wheelhouse. "Yes, Rebecca, I understand what you want me do. Do you want me to draft updates and releases and send them to you for review before sending out?"

"Yes," Rebecca confirmed. "Only draft an explanation when you believe there has been a shift, positive or negative, worthy of a comment. I will also be watching the stock price, and if I see something critical I will let you know."

"That sounds good. Is there anything else?" Kyle rose from his chair.

Rebecca rose shortly thereafter. "Yes, one more thing. I'd like you to sit in on every Executive Team meeting so that you will know firsthand any strategy or directional change that can help provide meaningful content for your proactive communications. Make sense?"

"Yes, it sure does." Kyle was smiling behind his serious demeanor. He had always wanted to be a part of the Executive Team. Though not a formal promotion or position, the privilege of joining this team was an honor he did not take lightly.

Rebecca closed with one last comment. "Kyle, I know you can rise to the occasion. Please read and research what other experts do in this arena. I want Cupcakes and Coffee to be known as the best communicator with its investors in the market. We will all benefit from doing so."

"I will. You can count on me." Kyle turned and left with an obvious spring in his step.

Rebecca smiled in return.

"Open or closed," asked Kyle as he turned after clearing the door.

"Closed is fine. I have to make a few more calls. Thank you."

She picked up the phone to dial another extension.

"Charles?"

"Yes, Rebecca. How may I help you?"

"Would you have time to review this week's sales and standard cost totals with me? I'd like to get a feel for how our week-on-week financial results compare. I am having to field some investor calls and need to be well informed."

"I'll be right there." Charles gathered a few folders and headed down the hall. In thirty-seconds, he was knocking at Rebecca's door.

"Come in."

"Hello, Rebecca"

"Hello, Charles. How are you doing?"

"Just fine, thanks. It's kind of a crazy time, isn't it?" remarked Charles.

"It sure is and I appreciate your instant availability. You probably dropped something important to do this, but it is necessary. I'm about to return many of these investor and analyst calls and I want to make sure I have as current and accurate information as possible." Rebecca spoke with a new-found vigor and confidence after her meeting with Brother Mark. Everything seemed a bit clearer now.

"Glad to help. So, where would you like to start?" asked Charles.

"Let's start at this week's week-on-week revenue." Rebecca began a long session during which she asked all the questions on her mind.

Charles and Rebecca spent about an hour going through every balanced score card metric while Rebecca took notes: total sales revenue, revenue segmented by food and beverage category, total customers served, average register ticket, standard direct labor cost per hour, fixed labor costs, standard occupancy charges, standard gross margin, SG&A expenses month and week to date, on-line customer survey scores, waste data, food ingredient commodity prices . . . all of these compared to the prior year. When all was said and done, she was as well prepared as she had ever been to field performance questions and calls from others.

Charles added, "Let me send over a spreadsheet with projected earnings per share and diluted earnings per share data based upon our current month trends. I think that will help calm whatever concerns our callers may have."

"That would be great. Thanks so much for your help."

"No problem. Do you want me to join you on the calls?"

Rebecca responded, "No, but please be available. I'll dial you if I get a question that I am not comfortable answering."

"Ok. I'll send that spreadsheet in five minutes." Charles turned and headed for the door.

"Thank you, again, Charles."

"You're welcome." Charles disappeared into the hallway.

Rebecca was parched after the long meeting, so she headed to the cafeteria for a beverage and to the restrooms for a much-needed break before her next task.

After stopping in the R&D kitchen to see what was brewing, literally, Rebecca headed back to her office.

She sat, scanned her e-mail, and saw the expected spreadsheet from Charles. She clicked on the attachment and viewed the earnings per share data promised. It made sense to her. She quickly typed a response to Charles with a simple message, 'Thanks.'

Now armed with everything she felt she needed, Rebecca grabbed the stack of message forms, thumbing through them to better gauge the time required. She sighed. This was going to be a long evening.

Since making it home for dinner tonight was unlikely, she decided to call Rick at his office.

"Hello, this is Rick."

"Hi Hon. How is your day?"

"Not bad. Just winding it up and getting ready to head home," Rick explained. "How about yours?"

"Well, not so good. I mean it was good, but I've got several investor calls I need to return before my day is over."

"Investor calls?" Rick seemed surprised. "I bet you've never had to do that before."

"No I haven't, but there's a first time for everything. I've been meeting with Charles and I think I'm pretty well prepared. Brother Mark was at Jerry's Again for lunch and he was able to help me think through the whole stock market thing pretty well."

"Based upon what you told me he said yesterday, I knew he had some useful insight. I am glad he helped you. But if you keep seeing him like this, I'm likely to get a little jealous," Rick said jokingly.

"You're lucky he has taken a vow of chastity." Rebecca played along. "No worries."

"Yeah, but more than one man-of-the-cloth has left God for the greener pastures of a woman."

"That's what it is? Greener pastures?!" They both laughed.

"Bad choice of words, but you know what I mean."

"I do. Anyway, I won't be home for dinner. Please save a plate back for me and tell the kids I'll be home before they go to bed."

"We'll miss you, but understand. Enjoy your calls. We'll see you at home later. Love you."

"I love you, too." Rebecca hung up.

Taking a deep breath, Rebecca took a few minutes to summarize her potential talking points if investors were to ask questions like, "So how are things going, or can you explain what you are doing to bolster the stock price?"

She wrote down these talking points on a spiral bound memo pad:

- Uninvited catalyst, to which we must adjust – not happy, but . . .

- Stocks trade on information, not on real value created or diminished.

- There is a gap between the market and our performance as a company.

- Our strategy hasn't changed (nor have our products, our talent, or our goals).

- Based upon our current measures, our business is good using week-to-week comparisons.

- Share week-to-week revenue and standard gross margin data points.

- Invite more questions/emphasize transparency.

Rebecca reviewed the list one more time. She was pleased and ready.

She grabbed the first message form from Mr. Anderson and dialed the number. She leaned back in her office chair waiting for the phone to be answered . . . the long evening had begun.

Finally, at about 9:15 pm, she had returned every investor and analyst call received that day. Though she got tired of hearing herself say the same thing over and over, she was satisfied that the inquirers were satisfied. Deep down, she hoped she might see a rebound in the stock price tomorrow.

Rebecca was beat.

Not bothering to clean-up anything in her office, and leaving her briefcase right where she left it after returning from lunch, she turned off her office light, closed her door, and left for home.

She worried. I hope I catch the kids before they go to bed.

Thinking Space

The next day began like any other day. The weather was not as nice as it had been. It had rained overnight and the sky was gray. The temperature was about ten degrees cooler. Rebecca dressed for the cooler and wet climate. She grabbed her coffee, said goodbye to her kids and Rick, and drove to the office.

Her office looked just like it had the night before . . . a mess.

Rebecca wasn't mentally prepared to execute her normal morning ritual of organizing her desk for the day. She headed for the cafeteria for a hot cup of coffee, and turned over in her head the thought with which she had awoken. Why do business leaders continue to harness their wagons to the idea that the purpose of business is to maximize shareholder wealth? Certainly, the people with whom she had spoken yesterday evening had.

After securing her favorite cup of cinnamon-cookie-flavored coffee, she headed for one of the many intentional 'thinking spaces' throughout the building. Architects who finished the building interior two years ago convinced her and the management team that these kinds of out-of-office spaces were not only trendy, but very effective at helping people generate out-of-the-box thoughts. The spaces were comfortable with tastefully done abstract art and chairs that looked like egg shells with built-in speakers for one's personal MP3 collection. Musical tastes drive different emotions in different people, so the personal approach was important – or so she was told. Small white boards resembling little slate chalk boards with a wide array of dry erase markers were available in the adjoining coffee table for doodling.

Rebecca hoped the architects were right. She needed to think. She found a space at the far-end of the building overlooking the small pond on the building's grounds that graced the southern edge of the property.

She placed her mug down on one of three coasters on the table. Why three? In an individual space? Odd, but not important right now.

She spent a few minutes staring out the window at the gray day and watching the ducks that were floating near the shore of the pond closest to the building. She thought to herself, it's a great day of weather . . . if you are a duck.

Closing her eyes, she began to reflect on the last three days.

Why do business leaders continue to harness their wagons to the idea that the purpose of business is to maximize shareholder wealth?

Last Friday, we were Cupcakes and Coffee, a private, closely held company, doing what we do best: providing customers with the most creative and best tasting treats on the planet. Today, we are Cupcakes and Coffee, a publicly-traded company, doing what we do best: providing customers with the most creative and best tasting treats on the planet.

Questions began to arise immediately . . .

So why have I just spent most of the last three days doing work for investors and not for our employees and customers? This was a simple, yet profound question.

What had changed? Why did my work change on a dime basically over the weekend? She was intellectually amazed by this fact.

Rebecca could count the number of times she even calculated the earnings per share on one finger in the three years since its inception. She had done so out of curiosity. She had never calculated diluted earnings per share.

Could it be that only the shareholders care? They care because they invest in a stock for the purpose of making a return on a speculative investment. It's easy to understand why they care. Debating herself, she thought, but why do business leaders care? Isn't this the question Brother Mark had asked . . . except he substituted the words 'harness their wagons' for the word 'care?' She pondered this series of thoughts for several minutes, staring at the gray day just outside the windows.

Brother Mark had used the term 'idea' as that to which business leaders harness their wagons. Was there an underlying thought or principle here? That question triggered some progress. Well sure there is! I remember it from my Intro to Business class in college, and then again multiple times while getting my MBA. Business leaders must care about shareholder wealth because that is the purpose of business, right?! That's what we were taught. No, that's what was undeniably, unequivocally pounded into our heads in business school. She got excited, feeling like she may have part of the answer.

Doesn't it make sense that if the purpose of business is to maximize shareholder wealth, that business leaders would do well to pay attention to it?! Her mind was playing hide-and-seek with the irrelevant, but at the time, necessary-to-answer question: who said that?

Rebecca started to think about significant writers she had studied over the years, Smith, Marx, Keynes, Veblen, Drucker, Barnard, Welch, Covey, Collins, Taylor, Friedman . . . .that's it! Milton Friedman said that or something close to that.[7]

That meaningless bit of trivia brought her consciousness back to the issue. Does the business leader have to care about shareholder value or stock price because that is the purpose of business? That does make sense, she thought, with the exception that prior to Monday, I, as the sole owner of Cupcakes and Coffee stock, didn't care one iota about the stock price. How does one reconcile that fact?

She marveled at how wonderful these thinking spaces were. The architects were right, she thought.

Rebecca took a couple of sips of coffee, never letting the edge of the cup more than three inches away from her lips. The warmth of the cup in her hands made her feel cocooned in the egg-shaped chair. She fancied, maybe I'll make this space my office and this 'egg' my desk chair.

Her thoughts continued, Prior to Monday I could have cared less

---

7 Friedman, Milton, *The Social Responsibility of Business is to Increase its Profits*, The New York Times Magazine, September 13, 1970.

about the stock price. And that was true for the three years prior, and yet our business was thought by many to be extraordinary! I won the Ernst and Young Entrepreneur of the Year award in 2011 for the Midwest. Our company went public at the asking price, making me an instant multi-millionaire. Was I a bad CEO because I didn't focus or concern myself with shareholder wealth?

She confessed to herself, truth be told, I did concern myself with the company in its entirety. It has been my baby from inception. Does that include earnings and value? Sure it does! But the focus was definitely on serving the customers; not on the value or wealth generated for me. The wealth came as a function of doing what we do extraordinarily well.

"That's it!" she exclaimed out loud, almost spilling her coffee in her lap. Wealth happened organically when we did what we did well, and, prior to this Monday, that is where I spent my time – on what we do. I didn't need to focus on shareholder value. It just happened.

Rebecca began a very brisk walk up the side stairs to her office. No time for the elevator. I've got to call Brother Mark.

Rushing by Carrie with a heavy breath and elongated, "Gooood mooorning . . .," Rebecca rushed into her office, shut the door quickly, sat down and started hunting for Brother Mark's business card.

Carrie thought first that Rebecca might have been sick. It was with that kind of urgency she was moving. But then she reasoned. Why would she be going to her office instead of from her office if she were sick? She hoped everything was alright given the IPO and all. Intuitively, she knew Rebecca was pretty stressed-out. When she saw a phone line was lit up from Rebecca's office, she at least knew Rebecca was alive. Carrie went back to work.

"Thank you for calling the Abbey. How may we help you?"

"I'd like to speak with Brother Mark Sculley, please."

The voice on the other end confirmed, "I'll connect you right away. Please hold."

"Thank you," Rebecca said to the on-hold music that filled her ears while waiting for Brother Mark. She hoped the music played at Cupcakes and Coffee while customers or investors were on hold was a bit more upbeat and happy. She'd have to check on that.

Mid-refrain on the chorus that was playing, the music stopped. "Hello, this is Brother Mark Sculley."

"Brother Mark, this is Rebecca Morton, the CEO at Cupcakes and Coffee."

"Of course, Rebecca! How are you this fine day?"

She wondered if he had looked outside yet today. "I am doing just fine thank you, but I do need to see you as soon as possible today. Is there any chance . . ."

Before Rebecca could complete her ask, Brother Mark interjected, "Oooooh, this is a tough day. The only time I have available today is right now until about 10:00 am. We have a community meeting then which requires my attendance. I also need to stay close because I am on call for any Abbey business office needs."

"Oh, that's a bummer . . ."

Brother Mark offered, "I'd be more than happy to meet with you if you could come over here."

"I can do that? Rebecca asked. "I thought there were prohibitions against visiting monks inside an Abbey."

Mark laughed slightly, "On one hand, you are right. Visitors are not allowed in the living quarters of the monks, but we do have several nice common areas in which visitors are welcome. I can reserve a small conference room and we can meet there. Will that work?"

Rebecca responded with enthusiasm, "That would be perfect! So what do I do when I get there?"

Brother Mark instructed, "Just go to the entrance on the west side of the Abbey chapel. There will be someone there to greet you. Just tell them you have an appointment to see me and they'll let me know you are here. It's as easy as that."

"Ok. I'm going to leave right now, so I'll be there in about five minutes. Thank you."

Wealth happened organically when we did what we did well.

"See you in a few minutes. Goodbye."

Brother Mark called down to the Abbey receptionist to let her know he was expecting a guest and to set aside the Abbot Sebastian room for their meeting.

Free Markets

Rebecca drove to the Abbey and spoke to the Abbey receptionist in right-at-six-minutes. "Hello, I am Rebecca Morton and I am here to see Brother Mark . . . Sculley" – she remembered his last name.

"Yes, he is expecting you. If you would just follow me, I will show you to your meeting room."

The Abbey was a beautiful building with a cathedral-like chapel and living quarters for the monks that looked like a British country estate with three stories of granite walls and framed windows. The roof lines were steep. The chapel roof line was framed-in by a steeple and crucifix on one end and a bell tower on the other. Two rock chimneys on either end of the living quarters highlighted the other roof line. The grounds were immaculate. The sense of peace at the Abbey was palpable. Rebecca felt very comfortable there, even though she had never stepped foot in the Abbey before.

The Abbott Sebastian room was very quaint with hardwood floors, a throw rug, and round table for four in the middle of it. One huge window dominated the east wall. The other walls were adorned with pictures of monks and priests from ages ago; at least by what appeared to be the age of the pictures. The walls were an institutional tan color, but lightened the room against the dark flooring. A lone overhead fixture provided the only light.

"Here you go! Brother Mark will be right with you."

"Thank you."

"May I draw you some water?"

Rebecca thought that was a strange choice of words and immediately wondered if they literally drew water from a well. Hesitating, considering the potential water born risks, she responded, "No, thank you. I am fine."

The receptionist smiled and politely departed with a simple, "Very well then."

After walking around the table once, surveying the room for what Rebecca thought was the best seat, she decided to sit where she could see both the door and the window. She thought to herself. I am not the average bear, as if chair selection was some kind of competitive activity. "Business people, what a sorry lot," she lamented in a whisper.

Brother Mark appeared, "Hello, Rebecca."

"Hello Brother Mark." Rebecca extended her hand in ritualistic fashion.

Brother Mark reciprocated and shook it honoring the common ritual.

"Please be seated." He took the seat opposite Rebecca, where he, too, could view both the window and the door.

Rebecca began the conversation. "So, do you actually draw water from a well here?"

"That's a strange question!" Brother Mark commented. "Why would you think that? Our Abbey has fully functioning city water and plumbing."

"No big deal, I was just curious." She knew differently.

"We may be traditional here, but we are not stuck in a technology warp. We have cable TV, though we don't watch it much, and wireless internet."

"Oh!" Rebecca acted surprised. "You're right!

After a brief pause, Brother Mark broke the silence and asked, "So, what is it you needed to see me about this morning?"

"Do you remember the heavy question you left me with yesterday at the end of lunch?"

"Yes. Something about why do business leaders focus so much on generating shareholder wealth," Brother Mark recalled.

"Close. You specifically asked why, given that there is little correlation between the stock market and real economic value created, do business leaders harness their wagons to the idea that the purpose of business is to maximize shareholder wealth."

"That sounds more accurate. Ok . . ." Mark waited patiently for the punch line.

Rebecca remarked confidently, "I think I have an answer for most of that, but I also have a very big question for you . . . something that I can't immediately reconcile."

"I am both glad and curious," encouraged Brother Mark. Leaning forward, he said, "Go ahead."

"Let's start where you started. We have a cultural or anthropological crisis in America. We have been taught to believe the purpose of business is to maximize shareholder wealth. That belief is attributed to Milton Friedman, a 1960's University of Chicago economist."[8]

"You've done your homework. Please, go on."

"It is logically easy to align the purpose of business defined this way and the weight and truth attributed to the stock market, stock values and related fluctuations – the beast as you called it."

"I agree."

"Is it any wonder that business leaders harness their wagons to this idea if shareholder wealth manifested in stock values are the primary metric for the purpose of business?

"That makes sense."

Thinking out loud now, Rebecca added, "And the invisible norm that governs behavior or culture, by definition, blinds us to other considerations. Maximizing shareholder wealth is a foregone conclusion for anyone in business. This is the cultural crisis to which you refer."

"I think you are right on."

"Except for one thing," Rebecca smiled coyly.

Brother Mark leaned back, "And what might that be Ms. Rebecca?"

"Until Monday this week, I was not focused on, nor did I ever measure the success or purpose of our company by our share price and value.

---

8 Friedman, op. cit.

Share value or shareholder wealth just happened as a consequence of doing what we do very well. So that means I am either the world's worst CEO and business leader, or that means that 'the purpose of business is to maximize shareholder wealth' idea is not accurate." Rebecca sat back indicating that her answer was now complete. She raised her eyebrows a couple times to prompt Brother Mark to react.

Brother Mark, leaning forward, slowly revealed a very wide smile. "So which is it? You are a bad CEO or the premise of the purpose of business is wrong?"

Rebecca shared, "With an appropriate level of humility, I think I am a pretty good CEO and the company results would certainly indicate that. But how can such a widely-held belief about business be wrong . . . for decades, no less?"

"Great question, but my research and study reveals that it is." Brother Mark leaned back and Rebecca leaned forward as if they were tethered together by an invisible wire between them. It was Rebecca's turn to listen.

"Go ahead."

Brother Mark began his explanation. "There is little if any doubt that the dominant ideology in business is 'the purpose of business is to maximize shareholder wealth.' Your education in your school of business would bear this out, would it not?"

"Absolutely."

"In order to really understand the tyranny of this belief, we'll need to roll this ideology back a little and begin with the premise of free markets, since that is the context in America in which we practice business."

Rebecca asked, "Why do we need to do that? Can't we just start at the dominant ideology being wrong."

61

Brother Mark retorted, "We can, but then we could not fully understand all the current dynamics and interplay between politics, government, the economy, and business. The interplay of these institutions contributes to the confusion and cultural crisis we now have. The current polarizing debates between the social liberal left and the libertarian right is really not about free markets, though their rhetoric would indicate otherwise. It's really about the dominant ideology and the consequences of that ideology in business and on people."

"I'm not sure I understand."

Checking his watch, which now read 9:30 a.m., Brother Mark continued.

"There is ample evidence and little debate that free markets offer the best solution for creating value, generating a standard of living for those subject to and working in a free market, and providing the opportunity for the poor or people on the lower end of the socio-economic scale to climb out of their impoverished circumstances. The Great American Experiment[9] is the best evidence of all for this, though there are many more examples of this truth."

Rebecca inquired, "The Great American Experiment? What is that?"

"From its inception, the world has viewed America as an experiment; founded over 230 years ago, as a free country, under God, with liberty and justice for all. Many were curious. It was a bold, inventive move by the leaders of this country to build a nation on a Christian moral code, a democratic form of government, of the people, by the people, and for the people, coupled with a capitalist economy."

"That is a different perspective. It must have been exciting for those in it and an oddity for those hearing of it and waiting to see what happened."

"Yes, you're probably right. Anyway, many of the technological

---

9 de Toqueville, Alexis, *Democracy in America.*

advances that have enhanced the quality of life of the domestic and world's population were born in America. America has been recognized as the world's leading economy for tens of decades now, though some think the bloom is off the rose."

"What do you mean by that?"

"Well, other economies have gained against the U.S. in both gross domestic product or GDP, life expectancy, and other measures of quality of life. Those gains are often attributed to U.S. shortcomings, which we'll address later."

"Ok."

"At a foundational level, free markets offer the best model for value creation.[10] The ability for a man or woman, or men or women to freely trade, barter, or exchange value for value, usually in the form of a product or service for currency, gives just about any person a fair opportunity to turn something at cost into something worth more than its cost, generating profit. As this cycle continues overall value is created in the economy. If you don't add value within an economic exchange, you don't earn profit."

"I'm with you."

---

10 Blessed John Paul II, Encyclical Letter *Centisimus Annus*, 42. "Returning now to the question: can it perhaps be said that, after the failure of Communism, capitalism is the victorious social system, and that capitalism should be the goal of the countries now making efforts to rebuild their economy and society? Is this the model which ought to be proposed to the countries of the Third World which are searching for the path to true economic and civil progress? The answer is obviously complex. If by 'capitalism' is meant an economic system which recognizes the fundamental and positive role of business, the market, private property and the resulting responsibility for the means of production, as well as free human creativity in the economic sector, then the answer is certainly in the affirmative, even though it would perhaps be more appropriate to speak of a 'business economy,' 'market economy,' or simply 'free economy.' But if by 'capitalism' is meant a system in which freedom in the economic sector is not circumscribed within a strong juridical framework which places it at the service of human freedom in it totality, and which sees it as a particular aspect of that freedom, the core of which is ethical and religious, then the reply is certainly negative."

There is ample evidence and little debate that free markets offer the best solution for creating value.

"Good. Most people are interested in improving their lot in life and providing for and protecting their families. This can be labeled as self-interest. Too often, self-interest is presumed to be born of bad intentions, but few find fault with it if we define self-interest this way. If, for the sake of argument, we differentiate self-interest, which most of us share, and selfishness, which we can define as self-interest born of bad intentions, perhaps we can make progress in our analysis."

"With these definitions, I share the positive self-interest motive."

Brother Mark affirmed, "Me, too, even though I don't have an immediate family, though I do care for my brothers here similarly."

"To support the positive definition of self-interest, which is widely shared, people must be able to own things. This gives them the chance to create value; by exchanging things at cost for something worth more than its cost. Private property rights are critical to the proper function of free markets. Rebecca, if you couldn't own shares in your company or own your own home, what would come of your self-interest? With what could you create value if you could not claim anything as yours?"

"I imagine nothing."

"I think nothing is right. Have you heard the term 'collectivism' before?"

"I've heard of it, but don't know what it means or its context. Can you clarify?"

"Sure. Collectivism refers to when things are owned collectively or by many. I'm curious. Do you have any rental properties in your neighborhood?"

"Unfortunately, yes. As you know, Atchison is filled with rentals."

"And how would you compare the quality or value of the rental properties to the owned properties in your area?" Brother Mark asked.

"There is no comparison. The properties owned by private citizens are taken care of, developed, and enhanced with the hope of increasing property values. Rental properties, on the other hand are often neglected."

"Exactly! The difference is in the ownership rights and the pursuit of positive self-interest. There is nothing to gain for the occupants of the rental properties so they tend to not care for the asset and let it deteriorate both inside and out. Common ownership or where private property rights are absent all too often results in a tragic loss of value. This is over-simplified, but represents the experienced outcome of many where collectivism prevails."

"I get it now."

"There is one other prerequisite for free markets. It's called the rule of law."

"Do you mean the existence of laws? Isn't that normal? Laws rule, don't they?" Rebecca wasn't feigning ignorance.

"The rule of law refers to laws that support and enforce the process by which free markets exist, and are governed. In order for a free market to function well, laws need to be consistently applied and predictable. These laws can put limits on what business can do, tax business, limit power, and protect the environment and citizens from potential business abuses. If a business or person owning property cannot reasonably predict the outcome of an economic transaction because these laws are subject to change, then it is more likely that an economic transaction will not occur. Lack of confidence in the set of laws or the rule of law can literally freeze a free market."

"Rebecca got excited, "I think I clearly understand that! The two laws that passed just this week have changed the legal landscape for businesses and individuals. That change has caused me to hesitate and view the future very differently. I can only imagine what the effect of that is when tens-of-thousands of businesses and business leaders hesitate like I have. It would be devastating to an economy."

"Yes it would and is," Brother Mark affirmed.

Checking his watch, Brother Mark suggested, "It's now 9:55. I am going to have to leave for the community meeting I spoke about earlier. There is much more to cover. Today is busy, but I could probably make some time for you tomorrow."

Rebecca was disappointed. She wanted answers and the dots between free markets and the flawed dominant ideology had not yet been connected. She shared an idea. "Brother Mark, would you be available for dinner tonight?"

"Well, we have vespers every night at 5:30 pm. I would be available after that."

"Great! Why don't you plan to join our family for dinner? I'd like you to meet my husband, Rick, and our children, Annie and Josh. I've talked to Rick about some of what you have shared with me. He has encouraged me to listen to you."

"I'm flattered on both counts. Thank you. I would love to join you for dinner. What time?"

"Let's plan on 6:30 p.m. Do you have a favorite dish?

"As monks, we eat whatever is placed in front of us. We are blessed with every meal. Please, whatever you fix will be delicious."

"Ok then, 6:30; my house; gruel for dinner." They both laughed.

"Before we adjourn, let's summarize our understanding so we don't lose the ground we have gained." Brother Mark's executive consulting experience was paying off now.

"Yes, let's," agreed Rebecca.

Brother Mark offered this summary:

- We have a cultural crisis in America that blinds us from the truth.

- The dominant ideology has governed business thinking for decades.

- Business leaders logically focus on shareholder value and stock prices accordingly.

- Free markets have proven to be the best vehicle for creating value for all.

- Private property rights are essential to the right function of free markets.

- The rule of law is essential for the right function of free markets.

- Absent private property rights and the rule of law, free markets and business leaders are subject to perversions.

Rebecca quickly responded, "Wait a minute, what was that last one?"

"We didn't talk about this but, in the absence of these two prerequisites for well-functioning free markets, those in business are subject to a variety of perversions that can kill the benefits of a free market," Brother Mark explained.

"I'll have to process that one, but if these prerequisites are required, it makes sense that something bad would happen if they were absent."

"Yes, something very bad can happen, and this begins to explain the false belief in the dominant ideology. But it will have to wait for this evening. I am sorry, but I need to go. It was a pleasure meeting with you. See you tonight." Brother Mark bowed as a courtesy and exited the room quickly.

Rebecca gathered her purse, pushed the chairs back to their pre-meeting position, turned off the light and headed back to her car. "Thank you," she offered as she strolled past the Abbey receptionist.

"You're welcome. Please come back and visit us."

The weather was no better than when she had arrived. She got in her car, switched on the wipers to clear her windshield of the moisture that had accumulated, and drove back to the office.

Office Work

Rebecca's office was still a mess, but the cleanup didn't feel like such a burden this time. In 15-minutes, everything was in its place and every place had its thing. Rebecca liked being organized. Perhaps that's why she was such a good problem-solver. If something was missing or out of place, she was determined to find its proper home.

She checked with Carrie to find out what was on her plate the balance of the day. Brent had left her a message. Before Rebecca called Brent back, she wanted to check the stock price. Part of her really didn't want to, but she felt compelled to do so. She had learned a long time ago to embrace the Stockdale Paradox: wake up every day, never losing hope, but facing the brutal reality of your circumstances.[11] She clicked on the NYSE favorites icon and up came the CUPC stock price as of . . . it was 11:05 CST.

It had leveled off. "Thank God," expressed Rebecca to herself. Though it was slightly down – a nickel per share – she felt the long night last night must have done some good. The feeling was reinforced

---

11 Collins, Jim, *Good to Great*, HarperCollins Publishers, Inc., p. 83.

when she saw the market was still in negative territory by well over 150 points. She felt fortunate and relaxed a bit.

She minimized the Internet Explorer window so that she could maximize and refresh it later that day to do another stock price check.

She dialed Brent. "Brent, good morning! I saw that you left me a message."

"Yes, Rebecca. We're getting some early responses from the survey you asked me to send out and I wanted to give you an update. Do you have time?" Brent inquired.

"Yes, I do. Please stop by when it is convenient."

"Thank you. I will be by shortly. Thank you. Bye."

Rebecca wondered whether the responses were skewed toward everyone wanting a pay increase, or whether everyone would understand that a minimum wage increase does not automatically warrant an increase for everyone. She feared the former and was pretty confident the survey results would bear that out.

Lunch was approaching and she really didn't feel like going out. Rebecca called Carrie and had her order in a deli sandwich from Marigold's, a quaint little sandwich and dessert shop in downtown Atchison.

She ate it in the quiet of her office as she caught up on industry reading; something she liked to do. Though she wasn't looking for it, she stumbled upon a little column article about the Cupcakes and Coffee IPO. The coverage was favorable and only mentioned her briefly. She was thankful for the gratuitous comments and nominal coverage. She had had enough of the white hot spot light over the last few days.

In the absence of these two prerequisites (private property rights and the rule of law) for well-functioning free markets, those in business are subject to a variety of perversions that can kill the benefits of a free market.

One of the feature articles caught her eye and she read it without returning to her sandwich or tea. It was entitled *Locked Down - The Lack of American Business Leadership Progress*. She'd always been a fan of leadership writings and had fancied herself a book author one day. The article, written by a well-known business school professor, analyzed and reported on the lack of progress in business leadership despite the tens-of-thousands of books written on the subject over the last several decades. His data was pretty compelling, since we are still talking about employee empowerment, involvement, and trust – 25 years after these topics were in vogue. Business people, what a sorry lot, she thought to herself.

Her mind began to play competitive thinking games again.

Am I one of the sorry lot? Are our leaders at Cupcakes and Coffee some of the sorry lot? I don't think so, but are we kidding ourselves? Why would we be different? Is there any real evidence that we are different in the things our leaders do here? All of these questions, and more, bounced rhetorically around in her head. She knew they were important questions, but intuitively, she knew now was not the time to seek answers or deal with what the answers might require of her.

She ended her lunch, dog-eared the page, closed the magazine, and set it aside on her 'good' reading stack for future reference. Rebecca brushed off her desk with the remaining unused napkin, tidied her work space, and threw the remnants of her lunch in her waste basket. Back to business . . .

Habit caused her to check her schedule. Dinner tonight! Brother Mark . . . I'll need to run to the store on the way home and will need at least an hour to cook something. What could we have?

Rick had always been the better cook, but it would be unfair to ask him to cook since she was the one who offered the spontaneous invitation to Brother Mark. Besides, Rebecca liked to cook. She just wasn't very good at it.

Thinking about dinner, she called Marj at Store #1. "Marj? This is Rebecca."

"Yes, ma'am! How's my favorite boss?"

"I'm fine, thank you."

"How may I help you?"

"Well, I am having a guest over for dinner tonight and I was wondering what you might recommend for dessert. I can pick it up on my way home? Anything new and delicious in your store?"

Rebecca knew full well there were a lot of new and delicious goodies in the store, but she learned a long time ago that a store manager's insight into trends and tastes was superior. She deferred to Marj.

"Oh, I think we can come up with something for you," feigning doubt and thinking. "How about a half-dozen of the new Sunshine Surprise cupcakes?"

Rebecca new these well. Sunshine Surprise cupcakes were made with yellow cake batter. The baked-in cavity in the middle of the cake was

filled with a delicious butter-cream pudding. The cake was topped with a white icing and yellow and gold sugar-glitter.

"Yes! Perfect. It'll help brighten this ugly day, too. Can you have them boxed up and ready for me by 3:30? I'll leave early so that I can get home to my dinner duties."

"Cooking tonight, too? That doesn't happen very often." Marj had learned a lot about Rebecca during her time at the company.

"Yep. Gonna break out something tried and true." Rebecca knew this was no time for experimentation with Brother Mark coming over.

"Rebecca, we'll have those ready for you."

"Great. Just put them on my account. Bye."

"Goodbye."

Brent stepped into her office doorway just as Rebecca was glancing at her schedule for the next thing to do.

"Is now a good time?" Brent asked.

"Yes, it is. What do you have?" Rebecca asked cautiously.

Brent entered and sat across from Rebecca at her desk. Rebecca leaned back with arms crossed.

Brent began, "As of noon today, we have heard from 268 store managers from 29 states. Seventy-seven percent of the managers responding so far indicate that their employees are asking questions similar to those in Store #1. Eighteen percent report there is no issue, and 5% report no questions yet."

This is precisely what Rebecca expected. She drew in a deep breath and exhaled. She thought for a moment in silence. Brent sat obediently waiting for a comment.

"We need to get out in front of this." Rebecca's competitive nerve and confidence kicked in. "We've been in similar circumstances before. I think it's appropriate to provide advice and direction to our franchise owners since we have experience."

Leaning forward, she stated, "Brent, please get with Anna (the Executive Vice President of Human Resources) and have her pull out the last policy statement we issued when we adjusted the lower pay grades to adjust for competitive wage pressures. About two years ago, we decided to adjust the starting and lower experience wage grades to improve recruiting and stem employee turnover as we grew."

In the back of her mind, Rebecca recorded that here is evidence that companies do increase wages without legislation requiring it.

"I sure will. Are you anticipating we'll do something similar in this circumstance?"

"Yes, it proved to be highly successful. Both our recruiting and turnover numbers improved. We had to shift the upper range limits of compensation to provide for adequate internal equity, but it only created room. It did not institutionalize automatic compensation increases; only the ability to earn more over time. This seemed to satisfy higher paid employees and provided the right incentive for our employees to continue to work hard and improve. In this way, we avoided creating an entitlement mindset when lower-level wage adjustments were made."

Brent remarked, "That's a brilliant way to handle this situation!"

"I hope so. It worked for everyone before."

Brent stood and turned to leave. "I'll get right on it."

"Thank you."

The discussion with Brent triggered more thoughts about the crisis pending on the heels of the new legislation. "Carrie?" as Rebecca buzzed her assistant.

"Yes, Rebecca."

"Will you please have Charles come see me as soon as he can? If he asks, tell him I want to do some financial projections considering the impact of the new laws."

"I'll call him right away."

"Thank you."

Rebecca was checking her e-mails when Charles stepped into her office.

"Good afternoon," offered Charles.

"Hello, Charles. Thank you for coming down so quickly."

"No problem."

"Have a seat." They both moved to her small conference table.

Charles sat, ready to listen.

"Ok, here is what I am thinking. As you can anticipate, the two laws passed this week could have a profound impact on our costs. We need to project the impact of these laws on our operating profits."

"Yes," responded Charles. "I've already been thinking about it."

"By Monday, I'd like to have a set of proforma financial statements with three different versions, anticipating the 15% increase in minimum wages and the employer participation in health insurance premiums for those post-employment."

"What three versions would you like?" asked Charles.

"I'm thinking about a low cost, moderate cost, and high cost version." Rebecca clarified, "The low cost version should be based upon only those making minimum wage or slightly more getting a 15% increase. The moderate cost version should be based upon some level below 50% of all hourly employees getting a 15% increase, and the high cost version should project financials with all hourly employees getting a 15% increase. While this version is improbable, if not impossible, it will allow us to quantify the real potential impact of this legislation."

"I understand." Thinking out loud, Charles shared, "I'll need to get with Anna to get information about the number of employees in varying wage ranges. I'll also need to get information about turnover and health insurance costs in order to complete the project." Charles sighed at the thought of the amount of work required to pull this off by Monday. "Whew," he exhaled.

"You are right. It's a lot of work and Anna holds the key to a lot of information. If for some reason she can't get you what you need in a timely manner, I can probably wait until Tuesday for the financials. Realistically, no one is asking for this information, but I don't want to get caught without knowing. We should know."

"I agree. We'll get going on this immediately," Charles shared confidently. "Should we pause work on the week-end financial metrics in order to ensure this gets done on time?"

Sensitively, Rebecca responded, "We need both complete. I know it's a lot to ask." She looked at Charles with eyes of compassion, but with no intention of taking the pressure off. Results matter. Nothing is free.

Charles expected her response, "Gotcha. We'll get it done. Thank you."

"Thank you, Charles. Please pass on my best to your team. I know they are working hard."

"I will." Charles exited Rebecca's office at a brisk pace that said, 'I have a lot of work to do.'

Rebecca returned to her desk to finish responding to e-mails.

The rest of the afternoon passed so quickly, she almost missed the 3:30 pm mark she had set to head home to begin her preparation for the dinner with Brother Mark. She packed up her briefcase leaving her desk in pristine condition. She thought to herself how nice it would be on Friday to come into a nice, clean office, unlike today.

The weather was starting to clear and the day was warming up. This was welcomed as she left the office to pick up her cupcakes at Store #1 and stop at the grocery store for the things she thought she would need for dinner. Her spirits were high and she was excited about the evening to come.

Part III

Dinner at the Morton's

The house smelled fantastic! Fresh whole wheat tortillas in the oven, freshly braised fajita meat on the stove, grilled veggies simmering on a burner. Lettuce, tomatoes, pico de gallo, and sour cream were already on the table.

Rebecca had straightened up the house when she got home and lit some candles to freshen up the stale air on the main floor. She had collected a bottle of Cabernet and a bottle of Chardonnay from their wine collection in the basement. Both were uncorked and ready to drink.

"Kids! Brother Mark should be here any minute!" Rebecca yelled. "Please wash your hands and come down for dinner."

Rick had been waiting in the hearth room for the invitation. He was relaxing after getting home with the kids and was thoroughly enjoying his night off from kitchen duties. He had already snuck a glass of Cab when Rebecca wasn't looking.

"Mmmmm. Smells great, Honey."

"Thank you."

Cupcake was resting on his dog bed in the hearth room after a fulfilling meal of gruel.

The door bell rang. Rebecca checked the oven clock and it read 6:28 pm.

Right on time, she thought to herself.

Rick, the kids, and Cupcake all arrived at the door with her to greet Brother Mark.

"Hello!"

"Good evening, Rebecca. Thank you for having me over."

"You're welcome. Please come in. This is Rick, Annie, and Josh."

Each reached their hand out and Brother Mark greeted each with an age-appropriate grip and shake. Annie and Josh behaved shyly and were a little afraid of the man decked out in the black habit. Cupcake bent his body in a figure 'C' trying to hide his excitement that his tail simply would not allow.

"Dinner is hot and ready. We're having fajitas. I hope that's OK."

"It smells wonderful! My ole factory lobes recognize the aroma."

"Please, join us at the table." Rebecca motioned to her right.

Brother Mark and the family followed obediently as Rebecca placed the dinner dishes on the table for a family-style meal. She poured the wine of choice for each adult and milk for Annie and Josh.

A few brief conversations and background information were shared during the meal, but mostly, the familiar sound of silverware on porcelain filled the dining room. It appeared everyone had enjoyed dinner, as there were only a few stray grilled veggies left when Annie and Josh helped clear the table.

While Rebecca and the kids worked in the kitchen, Rick and Brother Mark struck up a conversation.

"So tell me about your executive consulting business. Rebecca told me you provide this service to clients?"

"Sure. Well, having spent over 15 years in the marketplace, and having studied and continue to study enterprise leadership through my PhD, I feel like I deliver great value to my clients."

"Rebecca certainly has benefited from your insights. This is new territory for her – CEO of a publicly-traded company and all."

"I hope so. I value her inquisitiveness and passion for excellence. She is a tremendous asset to this community."

Rick acknowledged that fact with a brief nod.

"Before you arrived this evening, Rebecca mentioned that you two had been talking today about a dominant ideology in business and free markets. Can you share your thinking with me?"

Brother Mark recollected his summary notes from the conversation with Rebecca this morning, emphasizing Rebecca's role in uncovering the truth of the flaws in the dominant ideology.

Rick offered, "I agree that the dominant ideology is truly dominant. So much so, that I can't imagine a business leader embracing anything to the contrary. How do you get beyond that and introduce anything else to your clients?"

"That's a great question!" pondered Brother Mark.

"It's not always easy, but two concepts can act as bridges or gateways to something different. This is where Rebecca and I left off today, so it would be good to have Rebecca in on the conversation. Do you mind?"

"Not at all. Let's go to the living room where we will be more comfortable." Rick rose and motioned ahead. Brother Mark followed suit.

"Honey, we're moving into the living room. We're getting to some good stuff so you probably want to join us."

From a distant room, Rick heard, "OK, I'll be right there. Anyone want coffee?"

Brother Mark declined, but Rick responded, "Yes, please. Thank you."

They adjourned to the living room. Anticipating that Rick and Rebecca would sit together, Brother Mark sat in one of the high-back chairs facing away from the front windows. Rick sat on the couch.

Rebecca appeared carrying a silver tray with a small coffee pot, three small coffee cups, and three Sunshine Surprise cupcakes. The tray received 'ooohh's and ahhhh's' from both Rick and Brother Mark.

"Wow, those look delicious!"

"Help yourself whenever you are ready," shared Rebecca.

I can't imagine a business leader embracing anything to the contrary.

She settled next to Rick on the couch. Rick poured himself a cup of coffee and the conversation continued.

Rick narrated, "Brother Mark was just about to explain how he gets clients to consider something different than the dominant ideology in business."

Rebecca sat forward with her hands clasped around her crossed knee. It was obvious she was very interested in what Brother Mark was going to say.

"Yes, as I was saying, there are two concepts that can act as bridges or gateways to something different. Often, if you want to challenge the status quo that is fully entrenched, you must do so covertly, gnawing at the edges until you begin to reveal the truth."

Rick could relate to this strategy immediately because of his practice of law. Attorneys use this tactic all the time to get defendants to reveal the truth with their own words. Most people accused would never do this if the prosecutor simply claimed his or her belief in the truth.

Rebecca, on the other hand, found this strategy harder to grasp since she was used to facing and dealing with problems head-on.

Brother Mark continued. "I shared with Rebecca that, absent private property rights and the rule of law, free markets and business leaders are subject to a wide range of perversions; two of which form the gateways. The first and easiest for business leaders to comprehend is government intervention into free markets. Almost to the person, business leaders view government intervention as an imposition and burden to them."

Both Rick and Rebecca nodded their agreement with this notion.

"It's not hard to get business leaders to accept government intervention as intrusive. The next step is to consider that government intervention in the form of the lack of rule of law – defined as the consistently applied and predictable laws that provide for well-functioning free markets – is in itself, a perversion. A perversion is similar to an unintended consequence. Why?" prompting his own answer. "Because if a business owner cannot accurately predict the outcome of an economic transaction, then it is more likely the transaction will not occur. If you multiply this hundreds-of-thousands of times, you can have a devastating effect on the economy. Though, this was likely not the intended pursuit of the action, but an unintended consequence of the action."

Rebecca added, "Yes! I shared with Brother Mark that the two laws that passed earlier this week had that exact affect on me and my thinking."

Rick affirmed his understanding with a head nod.

"We are half-way home over the first gateway. Now that government intervention can be identified as itself, a perversion, the discussion with business leaders can now evolve into the purpose behind government intervention. This is where it gets really interesting. Let's make this discussion relevant for today. Rebecca? What do you think the purpose was behind the legislation passed this week?

Rebecca sat up, surprised that this casual gathering was going to require her to extemporaneously answer questions, though she was up to it.

"Well, I suppose one reason would be political. The more the government can do to help people, the more voters are likely to reelect the politicians endorsing the supposed 'helpful' measures."

"Good, but I heard sarcasm when you said the word 'helpful.'"

"Yes I did, because I don't see them as helpful at all, and I don't think many, if any, business people would."

"Fair enough. You've just identified the injection of one dimension of politics into the function of free markets. It's real and often clouds the core issue. But if we refrain from introducing our political biases into our assessment of the purpose of government intervention, can you think of another purpose behind the legislation passed this week that might get us closer to the core issue or problem?"

Rebecca thought for a moment, eye-balling the Sunshine Surprise cupcakes on the tray.

"At its core, I think the government is supposed to help people, so, extrapolating on that thought, one purpose of this legislation might be to truly help those who are struggling. I'll be honest. It's hard for me to not taint that thought with political bias."

"I fully understand, and while the bias is real, as you indicated before, getting to the core problem is critical for arriving at a good solution."

Rebecca understood this clearly. She could very much relate to this type of problem-solving process. A problem well-defined is half solved, she recalled to herself.

"Ok. So now we get to a debate about the role of government in a free market."

Rebecca chimed in, "Well that's easy. It's the rule of law as you suggested earlier."

"Yes, that's one role, but could it be that the role of government is to care for those in need?" Brother Mark suggested.

"I suppose so, but the government can't care for everyone in need," Rebecca offered, agreeing overall with Brother Mark's thought. "But they do such an inefficient and ineffective job. The politics just won't let the government be efficient and effective."

"You've said a lot there, Rebecca."

Rick was surprised at his wife's intuition about government and politics. She had never shown herself to be politically-minded.

"They are inefficient and ineffective, aren't they? All I have to do is think about my experiences at the DMV and I start to get hives. So I now ask . . . is it possible that while the government is intending to do good, as inefficient and as ineffective as they are, and as interfering as they may be in the rule of law, that they do so in the absence of something?"

The government can't care for everyone in need.

Both Rick and Rebecca looked at each other perplexed.

Rebecca spoke on behalf of both of them. "I suppose so, but what might that 'something absent' be?"

"Cupcake, anyone?" Brother Mark leaned forward to grab the cake closest to him. He peeled back the watermarked outer muffin paper and took a huge bite, as if trying to get to the creamy filling in the middle.

Still chewing his big bite and talking through his partially closed lips, knowing that doing so was poor manners, but anxious to show his enthusiasm for what was to come, he commented in a breathy voice, "Now we are across the first gateway and at the entrance of the second gateway." He wiped the edges of his mouth and licked his lips. "Amazing!"

Rebecca smiled at Brother Mark and then at Rick feeling a sense of pride at the compliment.

Brother Mark answered Rebecca's question with more questions. "Might that 'something absent' be a role that only business leaders can play, or a role for which they are best prepared? Might it be that one business leader's role is to care for those in his or her employ? Might it be that another business leader's role is to care for the community in which they work, looking beyond the four walls of the company to the common good of those inhabiting the same real estate?"

"That's an interesting idea," remarked Rebecca.

"Why so?"

"Well, reflecting on my experience, I have absolutely tended to that role at Cupcakes and Coffee. I care for my employees. I care and contribute to my community. It's one of the many keys to our success."

Rick, following the conversation, confirmed, "Yes, she has."

"Let me ask you this," offered Brother Mark, "how easy or natural will it be for you to tend to that role now; now that the stock of the company is publicly-traded?"

Rebecca replied, "Well if the last four days are any indication, I will have little time to do that. Most of my last four days have been preparing for and answering to investors."

"And would most people think you were being a good CEO doing such things?"

"Yes, but I don't think my employees necessarily would, given the role I played prior to Monday. The bar was set pretty high."

"But the investors would be pleased?"

"Yes, I hope so. That's why I am doing what I am doing."

"So you've adopted the dominant ideology."

Without thinking, Rebecca answered, "Yes." Hearing that come out of her mouth, she recanted, "No!"

"Herein lies the tension with which a business owner and leader must wrestle. How does one tend to the expectations of investors as key stakeholders and also tend to the needs of employees and the community?" Brother Mark took another large bite of his cupcake.

Rebecca admitted, "I know that tension."

Rick reached for a cupcake.

"The dominant ideology is quite suitable for a single-stakeholder mindset where investors trump all other stakeholders. The fact is, though, there are multiple stakeholders in any business."

Rick took his turn joining the conversation with a cupcake-filled, breathy voice. "Sure, there are vendors, employees, customers, citizens . . . and lawyers." Another feeble attempt at humor . . . Rick smiled with a little icing still stuck on his front teeth.

Rebecca elbowed him smiling.

"Yes, and they all deserve their due. The concept of human dignity manifested in a multiple-stakeholder mindset, is at the core of Catholic social teaching."[12]

"So are you saying that caring for all the stakeholders is supported by religious teaching?"

Brother Mark responded, "Yes, in a sense, but there is much more to it than that. Human dignity is just a foundation. Since it's getting late, and since that last cupcake is calling my name, I'd like to cover one last significant concept as we cross the second bridge or gateway. It's a very large hurdle in the middle."

"Go ahead," invited Rebecca.

"If we agree that free markets are the best option for creating value for all, and that value is manifested in the excess of what one pays over its costs, whether a product or service, then it is easy to understand that the consequence of value creation is wealth. Rebecca, you and Rick have become very wealthy with the value created in the market through Cupcakes and Coffee, agreed?"

"Agreed."

---

12 Compendium of the Social Doctrine of the Church, (UCCSB Communications, Washington, DC, July 2011), 144. "God shows no partiality (Acts 10:34, cf. Rom 2:11; Gal 2:6; Eph 6:9), since all people have the same dignity as creatures made in his image and likeness. " See also The Catechism of the Catholic Church, 1934.

How does one tend to the expectations of investors as key stakeholders and also tend to the needs of employees and the community?

"The dominant ideology would indicate that wealth generated is the property of the shareholder who put his or her investment money at risk. Those endorsing that ideology usually have no problem attributing the value and rewards earned in business to themselves as investors. On one hand, they are right. The ideology invites it. But wealth accruing to anyone is very, very dangerous. It is one of the single greatest perversions, if unchecked, that can accompany a free market that attempts to function without the rule of law."

"Keep going." Both Rick and Rebecca were intrigued.

"The problem isn't profit or wealth itself. I've heard it put this way. Profit is like oxygen. Oxygen is not the purpose of life, but it is necessary to sustain life. Likewise, profit is not the purpose of business, but it is necessary to sustain business. The core problem is a kind of self-reliance, independence, and complacency that can accompany great wealth generation and spawn a thirst for more than what one needs. This is commonly referred to as greed. Greed is the large hurdle in the middle of second bridge or gateway."

"Is this not positive self-interest as you put it this morning? What if someone just wants to take care of his or her family?"

"Great question. There is a very fine and delicate line between greed and positive self-interest. Greed, by any other name, is a version of selfishness; self-interest born of bad intentions. And it can doom individuals to suffering, both in this life and in the next. The love of money is the root of all evil[13], not money itself."

---

13 The Holy Bible, 1 Timothy 6:10, (RSV), "For the love of money is the root of all evils . . ."

"So the dominant ideology basically baits business leaders to unwittingly pursue that beyond which they need, committing themselves to a course of destruction?"

"Yes, but the negative impact is significantly more widespread than just on the business leader."

"How widespread?"

"Here is where the dots of the dominant ideology connect with free markets. Absent business leaders who can create value and properly deploy the resulting wealth toward the benefit of all stakeholders and the common good, the government is relegated to intervening to ensure that human dignity is preserved and the common good is served."

"So the 'something absent' resulting in government intervention is the lack of business leaders concerning themselves with the common good? Could this be the good that God intended for business and business leaders to do?"

"This is the role for which business leaders are uniquely wired and prepared. The belief and practice of the dominant ideology in business robs many business people of this role."

Rebecca offered, "But most of the business leaders I know are very wealthy and, while they live well, they are also very concerned about their employees and their communities."

"Yes, many are, and their ability to withstand the many perversions or unintended consequences of wealth generation are the subject of future discussions."

Brother Mark began to rise. "It's getting late and I must be going. Thank you for the wonderful dinner and that incredible yellow cupcake."

Rebecca interrupted, using the words that Brother Mark had used to wrap up their last meeting. "Before you go, let's summarize our thoughts so that we don't lose the ground that we have gained tonight."

Brother Mark returned to his seat without taking a step and thought to himself. *Well, well, well, an executive consultant is born.*

Rebecca summarized these notes out loud.

- It's very difficult to move beyond the entrenched dominant ideology in business.

- One primary gateway is government intervention aimed at caring for the marginalized in society, no matter the politics.

- Absent something, the government must intervene to protect the common good.

- Because of the wealth generated in and through business, business leaders are in a unique role to care for others.

- A huge obstacle in caring for others is the pursuit of that beyond what is needed or greed – a perversion native to free markets.

- Absent business leaders willing and able to serve the role of caring for others, the government must intervene.

"And . . .," Brother Mark hinted at something more.

"That's it, isn't it?"

"Using the resources and profit generated from business is the good that God intended for business to do." Brother Mark filled in the blank.

"That's a reach for me, but I understand the capability of business to do good in that way. Whether God intended that to be the case, I'll have to learn more before I can believe that."

"I fully understand your reservation and encourage you to think about that idea. I have and I'd be glad to share with you what I have learned when you are ready. Until then, keep wrestling with your role and be conscious of your choice to serve the multiple stakeholders with whom you have been entrusted. That's the best advice I can give you for both your business and for doing your part to reduce the level of government intervention and protect free markets."

"That's fair. I will. Want the last cupcake?"

Brother Mark smiled, gathered the last golden cake, and left shortly thereafter, having thanked Rebecca and Rick profusely for the privilege of the dinner and the company. Rick and Rebecca cleaned up the balance of the meal and dessert, put the kids to bed, and went to bed satisfied on a full stomach, a full head, and a full heart. It had been a wonderfully enlightening evening.

The Next Six Weeks

The next six weeks went very smoothly. Rebecca maintained a balance between serving and responding to shareholders and serving and responding to customers, vendors, and employees. This gave her tremendous satisfaction, both because it came naturally to her and she was good at it, and because she was doing her part to care for those entrusted to her while reducing the need for government intervention.

The two new Cupcakes and Coffee stores in California opened on time and on budget. New franchisees were identified in eight new emerging markets and plans for their first store openings were underway.

The IPO fever was beyond them and everyone at the headquarters appeared to be going about their business as they had been prior to the IPO. The stock price had leveled off and had begun to rise with the rest of the market. Though it wasn't back to its initial offering price of $15 per share, it was close and the future looked bright. No information other than the truth had surfaced in the market that played with the stock price. Investor calls had ceased and the company looked forward to filing its first 10Q with the SEC in 45 days.

The one cloud over the company was the pending financial impact of the legislation to raise the minimum wage and participate in paying health insurance premiums for the unemployed. Charles' financial projections were eye-popping! Even the lowest version, where only those making at or close to minimum wage resulted in a 2.5% reduction in gross margin and a 3.0% reduction in net margin. Rebecca was nervous about how to share that news with the investors.

The question about the good that God intended for business to do was still on her radar. She reflected on that often, especially as she became more conscious of her choice to serve everyone, including the investors. Though her faith was strong, it was still significantly void from her conscious work life. She just couldn't reconcile her belief that results matter and the good God intended for business to do. It seemed rational to her that bringing God into business would diminish business results.

She had seen Brother Mark a couple of times at lunch and had enjoyed some casual conversations about life and business. Neither of them had pushed the conversations much further.

The company was growing. Rick and the kids were good. Life was good.

Practicing Virtues

The pressure was building as the growth of the company, though controlled, was stretching resources to the breaking point. The company under Rebecca's leadership was happy chasing growth and hiring resources long after they could be absorbed in the costs and overheads of the company, but it now seemed like the company was floundering in multiple areas due to the strain. The finance area was especially troubling as the hunger for financial information for external consumption had grown exponentially. Franchise operations was another area that was struggling as newly opened stores needed extra support and planned stores were already consuming all that department's capacity.

Rebecca and Charles worked tirelessly to run the numbers and projections and they were concerned that if they added the resources now, when their historical profit or baseline was built on adding resources well after growth, that their first quarter common-sized financial statements would look worse than analyst's expectations. The fact that Rebecca had to even consider this was troubling her, but the brutal facts of her reality required it. Her heart would not let her forget the 60-plus hours a week the folks in these two departments were working week-in and week-out. She intuitively knew that that could not last much longer without significant negative consequences.

The financial impact of the recent legislation added more pressure to avoid adding resources. It would be hard enough to explain the impact on costs to investors without additional people resources complicating the story.

Adding God into this equation, who apparently intended business to do good, with what Rebecca anticipated would be diminished financial results, just didn't make sense. With the growing stress and tension between these issues, she was feeling overwhelmed.

"Rebecca?" came a request from Carrie over her phone.

"Yes."

"You have a visitor."

Wondering who it was, Rebecca headed for the door.

"Brother Mark! What a surprise! Rebecca approached him with hand extended in welcome. "What brings you here?"

"Well, I was praying for you and the company today, and I felt prompted to pay you a visit. The prompting was strong enough that I didn't want to chance missing you at Jerry's Again for lunch."

"Well, OK. I'm glad you are here. Please come in." Rebecca led Brother Mark into her office. He thanked Carrie as he went.

"This is a very nice office!"

Rebecca was a little embarrassed. "Well, I do spend most of my life in here." She felt the confession might help justify the few excesses that were in it . . . a couple of pieces of original art and an Italian marble statuesque in the corner.

After sitting at the small conference table in the office and helping herself to a butter mint, Rebecca said, "So, thank you for coming."

"Thank you for allowing the spontaneous meeting. I was worried I wouldn't catch you."

"Why the urgency and the prompting, do you think?" asked Rebecca.

"I think I can answer that. Ever since the discussions you, Rick and I shared after dinner at your house, I've been waiting for you to be 'ready' for additional thinking about the good God intends for business to do. I am hoping my prompting matches your readiness."

"This is really good timing. I am confident business does good, but I am struggling with the idea that God can help produce improved business results. Right now, the tension between the need to spend money and add resources, and the expectation of hitting analyst's projections is very stressful on everyone at the company."

"Perhaps I can clarify a few things and help you. Are you ready?"

Rebecca responded hopefully, "Yes, I am."

"If you would allow me, I'd like to start with an idea that supports one of your observations."

Rebecca, a little surprised and flattered, said, "OK."

"I remember you commenting that most of the business leaders you know, while wealthy, care a lot about their employees and the multiple stakeholders in their company."

"Yes, I said that," confirmed Rebecca.

"And it appears that though you are wealthy, you, too, care deeply about your employees and have been able to maintain a balance of care for all stakeholders. Am I representing you accurately?"

"It's been hard these last several weeks, but, yes, I think I have been able to do that. It hasn't been so much about the wealth, but about the pressure to serve the shareholders well. They are a new and significant stakeholder for me."

"I understand. I suggest that you, and others who care deeply for your employees, share a common set of beliefs that inform your values, your paradigms, and, ultimately, your behaviors. Would you say you appreciate and honor each person in your employ? That you respect their human dignity?"

Rebecca did not hesitate in her response. "Absolutely; regardless of their position."

"I experience you that way," reinforced Brother Mark. That made Rebecca smile.

Asking a question to redirect the conversation, Brother Mark asked Rebecca, "When I say the words virtuous and righteous, what comes to your mind?"

Rebecca thought for a moment, then responded. "Well, the word righteous triggers in me thoughts of someone who is better than others – not in a positive way. Especially if self-proclaimed, I think someone who is righteous thinks he or she is above someone else."

"Ok. What about virtuous? What images come to mind when you hear that word?"

"Virtuous feels much more positive to me. I don't know the actual definition of virtues, but unchanging, foundational principles come to mind. I suppose virtuous would describe someone who holds onto and practices unchanging principles. I suppose living a life of virtue would be desirable for many, including me."

"Yes, there is something in our nature that attracts us as humans to this kind of life. It is also a life to which God calls us.[14] Did you know that the Catholic faith has identified four 'cardinal' virtues?"

"I've never heard of 'cardinal' virtues. What does the word 'cardinal' mean?"

"Cardinal means 'of prime importance or chief.'[15] The cardinal virtues are the primary moral virtues that represent the foundation of natural morality. All other moral virtues extend from these four virtues."

Rebecca acknowledged her understanding with a nod.

"The four cardinal virtues are temperance, prudence, justice, and fortitude.[16] Prudence is more commonly referred to as wisdom, and fortitude is more commonly known as courage."

"I understand their general meaning and application, but help me understand how these virtues play into business and my role as a business leader," requested Rebecca.

"I will do that, but as I do, I want you to reflect on the dominant ideology, the benefits of free markets, the role and intention of government intervening in business, and the good God intended for business to do."

"I will."

"We'll start with the virtue of temperance. Temperance helps people

---

14 The Catechism of the Catholic Church, 1803, "A virtue is an habitual or firm disposition to do the good. It allows the person to not only do good acts, but to give the best of himself." 1804, "A virtuous man is he who freely practices the good."

15 http://dictionary.reference.com/browse/cardinal

16 The Catechism of the Catholic Church, 1805. "Four virtues play a pivotal role and accordingly are called 'cardinal;' all the others are grouped around them. They are: prudence, justice, fortitude, and temperance."

reduce their reliance on the world's goods.[17] This virtue is especially important for business people as they are frequently blessed with the resources to attain many of the world's goods and are, likewise, challenged with the temptation to do so."

Rebecca commented, "That makes perfect sense."

"The virtue of prudence or wisdom allows people to discern good from evil and the set of actions, right or wrong, that he or she will take based upon that determination. In a world where moral relativism makes good and evil an individual filter, this virtue is critically important. You can imagine how essential wisdom is for a business leader as he or she must make decisions regularly among competing options. Of course, one's worldview and beliefs play heavy in these decisions. A belief in the dominant ideology will tend to cause business leaders to make decisions consistent with the end of maximizing shareholder wealth. Wisdom would cause one to question that narrow field of vision and make decisions appropriate to perhaps different ends, say the common good," suggested Brother Mark.

Rebecca added, "What is good is often subjective. It makes sense that a deep belief in maximizing shareholder wealth would cause a business leader to make decisions consistent with this purpose and believe they are 'good.' But, if as you say, God intended business to do good, then concern for jobs and livable wages should be a concern for business and business leaders."

"Yes, precisely," affirmed Brother Mark.

He continued, "The virtue of justice concerns itself with the human dignity of each person and the due each person deserves.[18] A sense of,

---

17 The Catechism of the Catholic Church, 1809. "Temperance is the moral virtue that moderates the attraction of pleasures and provides balance in the use of created goods. It ensures the will's mastery over instincts and keeps desires within the limits of what is honorable."

18 The Catechism of the Catholic Church, 1807. "Justice is the moral virtue that consists in the constant and firm will to give their due to God and neighbor. [...] Justice toward men disposes one to respect the rights of each and to establish in human relationships the harmony that promotes equity with regard to persons and to the common good."

and belief in justice demands that business leaders concern themselves with the lives of those with whom they have been entrusted."

"I can relate to that. That explains a lot of what I feel every day."

"I imagine it also explains why so many business leaders of whom you speak care for their employees. It's in our nature. Unfortunately, the dominant ideology can blind many of this role and the good God intended for business to do," added Brother Mark.

"Last is the cardinal virtue of courage.[19] Think about the kind of courage or fortitude a business leader must have to fight the entrenched dominant ideology. You have probably been experiencing this the last several weeks," suggested Brother Mark.

Rebecca replied, "Yes, I have, but I fear that my courage has waned as we approach our first quarter reporting date. I haven't made some decisions that my wisdom and sense of justice might dictate."

"Even though you knew nothing of the cardinal virtues before this discussion, you have had a natural inclination to live these. That's why these are referred as to as the foundation of natural morality, or cardinal virtues."

Rebecca nodded.

"Do you mind if I get a glass of water? I've been talking too much!"

Rebecca rose immediately and asked Carrie to deliver two glasses of ice water to her office. Brother Mark continued.

"Now I want to connect three significant dots. The natural or cardinal virtues are the force that causes business leaders to tend to the good God intended for business to do. Is that relationship clear?"

---

19 The Catechism of the Catholic Church, 1808. "Fortitude is the moral virtue that ensures firmness in difficulties and constancy in the pursuit of the good. It strengthens the resolve to resist temptations and to overcome obstacles in the moral life."

"Yes, I think so. It is a force that is contrary to the force and inertia generated by the dominant ideology."

"That's very good insight," offered Brother Mark.

"The practice of cardinal virtues, allowing business leaders to practice the good God intended for business to do is a counter balance to government intervention."

Rebecca looked puzzled. "I'm not sure I understand."

"Let's look back to the core purpose, absent politics, of why the government intervenes into business. They do so to ensure the pursuit of the common good and to protect human dignity. They do this in the absence of business leaders who concern themselves likewise. This next point is critical. Because of this causal relationship, the level of government intervention is inversely proportional to the level of virtues practiced by business leaders." Brother Mark paused, waiting for Rebecca to digest this point.

Carrie appeared with the glasses of water and placed them on the table.

"Thank you, Carrie," offered Rebecca. Brother Mark gave her an appreciative nod.

After taking a long swallow of her water, Rebecca spoke. "That's big. So you are suggesting that the government must intervene if the practice of virtues among business leaders is lacking."

"Yes, I am."

"Today, most business leaders would acknowledge the level of government intervention is very high. If this inverse relationship is true, then that would indicate the practice of virtues in business is neither very high nor very common."

"Yes, and I believe that is significantly fueled by the widespread and unquestioned acceptance of the dominant ideology," clarified Brother Mark.

Rebecca presupposed, "If the inverse is true, then improvement in the practice of virtues in business can reduce the level of government intervention?"

"Yes, that's exactly right. Catholic social teaching also reinforces that the primary role for addressing issues of human dignity in the workplace is the business leaders', not the State's or government's role.[20] If we don't tend to our role as business leaders, the government acts to ensure human dignity and the pursuit of the common good."

The level of government intervention is inversely proportional to the level of virtues practiced by business leaders.

"This has significant implications in the political realm as well. The polarizing argument about free markets is, in truth, founded in this tension; not in a debate about free markets. Free markets are still the best choice for producing value for all. If we want more unencumbered free markets, creating more value for all, it is incumbent upon business leaders to practice virtues. Freedom is imperative for any individual to choose between right and wrong, and virtues predispose one to do the good. Absent the practice of virtues by business leaders, the structure that allows for the proper functioning of free markets creates substantial opportunity for business leaders to choose otherwise. Does this make sense?" asked Brother Mark.

"Yes, it does," replied Rebecca.

"This leads us to the third significant connection to make. Living a virtuous life as a business leader is not easy, nor is it free. The

---

20 Blessed John Paul II, Encyclical Letter, *Centisimus Annus*, " . . . primary responsibility in this area (overseeing and directing the exercise of human rights in the economic sector) belongs not to the State but to individuals and to the various groups and associations which make up society."

temptations of success and wealth are significant. In the Bible, Jesus shares this thought with his followers. 'It is easier for a camel to go through the eye of a needle than it is for a rich man to enter the kingdom of God'."[21]

"I will translate that as nearly impossible," commented Rebecca.

"Yes, very difficult, I imagine."

"In the book of James, the Bible states, "But the one who is rich should take pride in his low position, because he will pass away like a wild flower. For the sun rises with scorching heat and withers the plant; its blossom falls and its beauty is destroyed. In the same way, the rich man will fade away even while he goes about his business."[22]

Rebecca thought about what she had just heard and swallowed hard. That hit a little too close to home.

"And finally, 'No one can serve two masters. Either he will hate the one and love the other, or he will be devoted to one and despise the other. You cannot serve both God and money.'"[23]

"You know the Bible well," Rebecca complimented Brother Mark.

"Thank you. Does that surprise you?"

"No."

Brother Mark continued, "A pearl of great price is not to be had for the asking. In the gospel of Luke, Jesus emphasizes the price people must pay in order to become disciples. He shared, "Suppose one of you wants to build a tower. Will he not first sit down and estimate the cost to see if he has enough money to complete it? For if he lays the foundation and is not able to finish it, everyone who sees it will

21 The Holy Bible, Mark 10:25 (NIV)
22 The Holy Bible, James 1:10-11 (NIV)
23 The Holy Bible, Matthew 6:24 (NIV)

ridicule him, saying, 'This fellow began to build and was not able to finish.'"[24]

"Similarly, business leaders must consider the cost of leading in business. Most business leaders see and are romanced by the upside. Few consider the downside or cost of doing so. The downside referred to here is not bankruptcy. The downsides here are the temptations and perversions that accompany wealth generation on the heels of value creation. Living a virtuous life is the price only business leaders can pay to protect free markets and the related benefits." Brother Mark rested. "Nothing is free."

Rebecca leaned back, contemplating what she had just heard. Her office was silent. Both took several sips from their water glasses during this time.

Brother Mark prompted Rebecca, "What are you thinking?"

"Well, I am thinking two things. First, I am thinking how ignorant I have been in the pursuit of my career and business goals: ignorant of both the good God intended for business to do, and the price only I can pay as a business leader to protect the benefits of free markets. It's not that I didn't know business did good or that caring for others was part of that effort, but I had no idea God and my faith were to be an integral part of that."

Rebecca continued, "Second, I am thinking how thankful I am, in spite of my ignorance, that Cupcakes and Coffee and the people that make up the company are hearty, healthy, and here. I can only chalk that up to the grace of God, because I have neither been conscious of or appreciative of His hand in matters concerning the company. That's big."

"Yes it is."

Rising slowly, Brother Mark commented, "I think I should leave

---

24 The Holy Bible, Luke 14:28-30 (NIV)

you with your thoughts. I am available at the Abbey if you have any questions about what I shared. I encourage you to read the Bible verses I shared with you. If it's Ok, I'll check in with you tomorrow."

Rebecca was lost in a fog of thoughts and emotions. "Yes, thank you so much for coming. I think your prompting was right. Thank you for the courage to come over without an invitation today." She paused, looked at Brother Mark, and confessed, "I think something significant just changed."

Living a virtuous life is the price only business leaders can pay to protect free markets and the related benefits.

Brother Mark smiled.

Rebecca reached out to hug Brother Mark, who accommodated her outstretched arms. Sometimes a handshake just doesn't do a relationship justice.

Brother Mark turned and left after saying, "Goodbye."

Rebecca followed him to the door and shut it, asking Carrie to hold her calls. She sat back down at the table, put her head in her hands, and cried.

New Life

Rebecca couldn't remember the last time she had cried. Her tears weren't tears of sorrow or regret. They were mostly tears of gratitude; not the typical rational gratitude that we all recite in prayer for a meal or when something good happens or if the sun is shining. It was a deep-seated, soul-wringing gratitude that only one knows when something miraculous happens like the birth of a child, or a person gives up his or her life for another.

This entire process with Brother Mark had revealed so much truth, that it all made sense now. Politics made sense. Government action made sense. Free markets made sense. Business doing good made sense. The price only she could pay as a business executive made sense; and pay she would. It was essential for all of the above to prosper and tend to their specific role in the proper order of things.

The urgent items of the day seemed trivial now. There was no way she was going to get anything done the rest of the day at the office. She had to tell someone, so she called Rick to see if he was available for lunch. Luckily, his lunch appointment for the day had canceled. They agreed to meet at Jerry's Again in ten minutes.

Rebecca did one last check of her e-mails, packed up her briefcase, and told Carrie that should would be out of the office the rest of the afternoon.

Curious after seeing Rebecca's eyes, Carrie asked, "Are you Ok?"

Rebecca stopped, looked Carrie straight in the eyes, and shared, "I have just learned the lesson of a lifetime. When the time is right, I will share it with you. Honestly, I cannot remember the last time I felt this good." With a broad smile, Rebecca headed for the elevator.

Carrie shrugged and wondered what in the world could have happened in her office earlier.

Rick met Rebecca ten minutes later at Jerry's Again.

After navigating through the maze of tables to Rebecca, Rick sat down with a wave and smile in the direction of Liz, the owner/manager.

"You've been crying!" Rick remarked softly, though with surprise. "What happened?" He appeared concerned.

Embarrassed, Rebecca responded, "That's why I wanted to have lunch with you; to explain my morning. It was wonderful."

"Wonderful?! But you're crying," talking through his clenched teeth leaning in, "How wonderful could it have been?"

"Don't worry, everything's Ok."

The server stopped by the table and took their drink orders. Since they both knew the menu well, they both ordered their meals at that time. That way there would be fewer interruptions while Rebecca explained herself.

After their waters arrived, Rick sat back in his chair, "Well . . ."

"Brother Mark visited the office this morning, uninvited. I have been struggling with the stress of balancing the need we have for more employees and the need to serve the shareholders. You know this."

"Yes, I do."

"He responded to a 'prompting' – he called it, to visit me feeling that I may be ready to hear more about the good God intended for business to do. He was right."

"And this made you cry?"

"Well, yes, but it was the truth revealed in the conversation that was overwhelming for me. It was amazing." Her eyes welled-up with tears again.

Rick acknowledged, "You have my attention."

Rebecca began explaining in detail the cardinal virtues and how critical they are for business leaders to reduce reliance on the world's goods, to discern right from wrong, to respect the dignity of each human being, and to have the courage to fight against the dominant ideology in business. Rick listened obediently.

She continued by explaining the three significant connections, beginning with the idea that virtues are necessary for business leaders to do the good for which God intended business to do. She followed with the thought that the level of government intervention is inversely proportional to the level of virtues practiced by business leaders. This revelation shocked Rick, too.

"So you're telling me that the liberal leftists intervention in business is a response to the lack of practice of virtues by business leaders?"

"Yes. And it makes even more sense when you think about the fact that the 'liberal leftists,' as you call them, have no other tool but government to use to right the injustices that all too often accompany business in practice. They are only doing what they can with what they have."

"Wow. I get it, but I'm shocked."

"The last significant point made, and the one that really blew me away, was that living a life of virtue as a business leader is neither easy nor free." Rebecca hesitated as she swallowed back tears. "Rick, I have functioned my whole life in business and excelled. I have excelled in spite of my ignorance of the price to be paid to live virtuously in a marketplace filled with many who are not. I can only explain that by and through the grace of God. I am not that strong and I am not that good." She looked down as a tear hit the napkin in her lap.

"I am just so grateful today for these revelations. I honestly can't believe it. Everything fits and makes sense now. I feel so content and complete."

"I can tell."

Their lunches came and the two ate leisurely, sharing more of their thoughts and insights about what was learned today. They realized both had taken their career successes for granted.

After the meal, Rick returned to work and Rebecca went home to relax, think, and pick-up the kids from school. This was the first time in months she had chosen to make picking up the kids a priority.

Both Annie and Josh were shocked to see their Mom waiting for them when school let out. They ran to Rebecca and shared big hugs.

The evening with Rick was warm and comfortable, with light conversation and an almost giddy mood. Rebecca was stealthily contemplating work tomorrow. There was no longer a sense of stress and no longer a feeling of tension amongst competing needs. The clarity was liberating. She knew exactly what needed to be done.

At some point during the evening, Rebecca began to reflect on her GMA interview from months ago. Over a period of hours, she thought to herself. Well, I acted like a lady today and cried when I felt like it. Not like a man! It felt good. Am I poised now to make a significant difference at Cupcakes and Coffee? You bet I am! I've paid a price for the success we have had, but I have not paid the price only business leaders can pay to protect free markets.

She remembered the 'Nothing is free' subtitle on Brother Mark's business card. Incredible.

The evening ended early with great anticipation for the day to come.

A New Day

Rebecca arrived later than normal to work after taking her kids to school. She walked briskly past Carrie, issuing another extended, "Gooooood moooorning," on her way to her office.

She sat her briefcase down to her left and dialed Charles' extension. Charles picked up after the first ring.

Sounding tired, Charles answered, "Hello, Rebecca. How may I help you?"

Rebecca responded, "Good morning, Charles. I was wondering if you could come down to my office. I'd like to discuss something with you."

"Sure, I'll be right down." Charles responded appropriately, but dreaded getting another assignment on top of his department's already significant workload. It was widely known that when Rebecca called, there was always work to be done thereafter. He headed to her office.

"Hello, Charles," meeting Charles at her door. "Please sit," pointing to a chair at her small conference table.

"Hello." Charles sat obediently.

Rebecca began, "Charles, I know you and your team have been working like dogs to stay on top of the new demands for the financial information for external consumption. Thank you and your team for your hard work."

"You're welcome," Charles said politely, but he anticipated the bombshell ask to follow.

"I want you to immediately hire the three positions you've asked for."

Charles almost fell out of his chair. "But what about chasing growth and deferring people additions until absolutely necessary? What will the shareholders think if our SG&A costs go up disproportionately to sales revenue?"

"Consider this absolutely necessary. What will they think if we do not concern ourselves with our people, work them to death, and potentially cause accumulated industry knowledge to leave the company? That is not an acceptable outcome to me, and I don't believe that will be an acceptable outcome to them."

"Rebecca, thank you." Charles expressed an audible sense of relief.

"All I ask is that you look at all options before adding these people including job consolidation, cross-training, and looking across the company for skilled, under-utilized people. And don't take too long doing this. You need to get relief."

"I'll do that. What do I tell Anna?"

"I've already sent her an e-mail and to expect a visit from you today. She knows I support your requests for additional people. Expect her to serve you promptly and thoroughly."

"Wow." Charles shook his head. "I'll do that on my way back to my office. Is there anything I can do for you?"

"There is nothing you can do for me right now, but thank you. You've done plenty. Just keep doing what you are doing." Rebecca rose and saw Charles to the door. They shook hands and parted with smiles.

One down and one to go, thought Rebecca.

She dialed Brent's extension and invited him to her office. Brent was there in less than 30 seconds.

"Hello, Brent. Please sit," pointing to the same chair Charles had just vacated.

Brent sat down obediently.

"Brent you and I have talked about the effect the ramp up of new stores has had on your team."

Brent confirmed, "Yes, we have."

"I don't expect the addition of new franchisees and new stores to stem any time soon."

Here comes the work, thought Brent to himself.

"I'd like you to add a New Store Service and Support Manager to take a significant amount of that workload off of you, specifically, and I'd like you to add the two New Store Project Managers you asked for months ago."

"But what about chasing growth and only adding people when absolutely necessary?" Brent retorted.

"Consider this absolutely necessary." The balance of the conversation went like the conversation Rebecca had just had with Charles. Brent appeared excited and re-energized when leaving her office.

Rebecca touched base with Carrie and began her new routine of intentionally visiting with managers and employees in the company about key issues and obstacles they were facing. She believed that the best thing she could do to add value to everyone and to do the good God intended for Cupcakes and Coffee to do, was to serve those serving the customer or to serve those serving those serving the customer. It really was that simple in her mind.

Though shareholder expectations had not diminished, any worry about the shareholders and their expectations had disappeared. She was confident that by living the virtues as CEO of Cupcakes and Coffee, that value created for everyone would increase.

Her logic told her that this link between practicing virtues at work and value creation must be clarified further. She had some ideas on how to do that, but wanted an executive consultant to check her. That afternoon, she called and invited Brother Mark to her office.

Effective Leadership

"Rebecca, Brother Mark is here to see you."

"Thank you, Carrie. Please send him in."

Brother Mark peeked into Rebecca's office before entering. "Good afternoon."

"Hello, Brother Mark! Thank you for coming. Please come in and have a seat." Rebecca motioned to a seat at the small conference table. Beside the table was a small, rolling white board stocked with different colored dry-erase markers and an eraser.

Rebecca had ordered two Sunshine Surprise cupcakes for their meeting. Brother Mark's eyes lit up when he saw them on the table.

Seeing Brother Mark eye the cupcakes, Rebecca said, "Yes, those are for us. Help yourself."

He did, digging into one of the cupcakes with a mouthful and smile. "Thank you," in the uniquely breathy voice of one snarfing a cupcake.

Rebecca watched him enjoy the literal fruits of her company's labor. She asked Carrie to bring in two glasses of ice water.

Sitting back and rubbing his tummy, Brother Mark let out a satisfied, "Ahhhhh."

"So, how have you been?" asked Brother Mark.

"I've been fantastic. It's been a good day."

"Oh, yeah? How so?" Brother Mark was curious.

"Well, the overwhelming clarity and gratitude from yesterday have not diminished. As I thought about my role and the things I must do to live the virtues at work, it was clear what needed to be done." Rebecca went on to explain the meetings with Charles and Brent earlier that day and why those decisions were so important and further evidence of her commitment to serve all stakeholders, not just shareholders.

"I see," responded Brother Mark.

"There is still one piece missing, though. I think the link between living the virtues at work and enhanced value creation is thin or missing. I'd like to offer an answer and get your opinion. That's why I invited you here today."

"Got it! I am excited to hear your thoughts in this regard."

"Please let me start with what changed in me yesterday," requested Rebecca.

"Ok."

"Having learned more about the cardinal virtues and how my faith fully aligns with and is necessary for my role as the CEO of Cupcakes and Coffee, I am free to be an integral person. Even though I was not consciously withholding my faith from my work, I certainly was not consciously acting on what I know and believe to be true. The key to me was understanding that if I want human dignity to be paramount and the common good to be served, then it is my responsibility to shine a light on these things and act consistently with my beliefs. In doing so, I do my part to minimize government intervention, enhancing the rule of law which serves to protect the benefits of free markets. This gives us a chance to continue doing what we do best; providing the most creative and best tasting treats on the planet."

"That's a nice summary."

"The confusion over who to serve; the shareholders or other stakeholders, is gone. It is clear to me that when we live the virtues and serve those serving the customer that all stakeholders are served well. This new business ideology is incongruent with the dominant ideology, and is much more true to the good God intended for business to do."

Rebecca continued by drawing on the white board *value creation* on the left and *practicing virtues* on the right. While her intuition helped her see how the two were connected, she placed a big question mark between the two, indicating that something was missing to explain the direct impact of the practice of virtues on value creation.

Brother Mark asked, "So, what are you thinking about this question mark?"

"You know I am an avid reader of anything on leadership. It's been my passion and love for years."

"You've shared that with me before, yes." affirmed Brother Mark.

"The gap between practicing virtues and value creation is filled by leadership." She wrote the word above the question mark.

Brother Mark studied the board, but remained silent.

"Here is what I know and believe about leadership. The role of any business leader has two components; one is that of management and the other is that of leadership. Operations are managed and people are led. Operational management refers to a business leader's technical ability or their 'how to' knowledge. To be successful in business, a business leader must know how the world works, and how their business can be designed to function effectively and efficiently. Does that make sense?"

"Yes. In my business and in my role at the Abbey, I must know how to do the job I have been assigned and be able to help others perform the role they have been assigned. I believe that correlates to the 'manage operations' role of a business leader."

"Yes."

"The leadership role, on the other hand is about people, and specifically getting them to 'want to' do the work. This role is about one's cooperative competency, or his or her ability to get others to cooperate in the work, not his or her technical competency."

Brother Mark remarked, "What is that term 'cooperative competency?' I've not heard that before?"

Surprising Brother Mark, Rebecca asked him, "Are you familiar with the Old Testament Bible verse in Ecclesiastes 4:9?"

"So the student becomes the teacher." Brother Mark smiled. "Yes, I recall that verse. In the RSV translation of the Catholic Bible, the verse reads, 'Two are better than one because they have a good reward for their toil.'[25] In some Protestant translations, the verse reads, 'Two are better than one because they have a good return for their work.'[26]" Rebecca wrote *Eccl 4:9* beside the question mark in the gap.

"You didn't let your student down." Rebecca smiled in return. Brother Mark nodded playfully to acknowledge her compliment.

"So why is this verse important?" queried Brother Mark.

"Great question. This verse is critical to our understanding of leadership, because in it is the natural truth of God's Plan; the key, if you will, to business doing the good that God intended for it to do."

"Really . . ." Brother Mark was fully attentive. This was new territory for him.

"Many Christians believe that doing business, creating value, and accumulating wealth, tithing to the Church, and being charitable are the ultimate manifestation of their faith. After yesterday's truth telling session, I believe otherwise."

"Do tell more . . ." Brother Mark leaned in to hear.

Rebecca turned to the white board, "I believe it is fair to translate this verse to mean that when two people work together or cooperate fully and willingly in the work at hand, their reward can be significant. In this way, the whole becomes greater than the sum of the parts."

Brother Mark nodded his understanding.

"Leading people, the second component of the role of any business leader is to get others to commit fully and willingly to the work at hand. Leadership is not required if the work requires just you. Leadership is absolutely required as soon as the work requires more than just you." Rebecca paused to check on Brother Mark.

---

25 The Holy Bible, Ecclesiastes 4:9, (RSV)
26 The Holy Bible, Ecclesiastes 4:9, (NIV)

He was deep in thought.

"Leadership can best be defined as the art of optimizing cooperation. Why? Because the more people are fully and willingly engaged in the work at hand, the greater the reward or return. Translated . . . the more value they create. The business leadership buzz words for the result of people cooperating more are agile, empowered, and trusting."

The lights started to come on for Brother Mark.

"The ultimate measure of business leadership and management is the value created for all, but the measurable output from leadership, an interim measure of success, is the level of cooperation, since the level of cooperation is directly correlated to the level of value created."

"I buy that," commented Brother Mark.

"The only remaining question, then, is, 'Does practicing virtues at work enhance cooperation or hurt cooperation?'

Brother Mark offered some more questions, "Or, are people more likely to commit fully and willingly to the work if their leader is courageous, wise, tempered, and just? You used the term 'integral' earlier to describe where you are. Is an integral person more likely to enhance cooperation?"

After a brief pause, "And your answer is . . ." Rebecca prompted Brother Mark.

"Well, certainly that is true."

"I believe so, too. The final connection between practicing virtues at work and creating value is all about effective leadership. Defining leadership as the art of optimizing cooperation, supported by the idea that two are better than one because they have a good return for their work is a lynchpin."

"I get it. Wow!" replied Brother Mark. He smiled, still studying the board.

"So why has business made so little progress over the last 30 years in their practice of effective leadership? As we shared months ago, we are still struggling with employee empowerment and trust building! I believe the lack of gains can be explained by the incongruence of the dominant ideology with the basic premise that two people, fully and willingly cooperating in the work at hand, create better value. The selfish pursuit of personal wealth is incongruent with getting others to cooperate in the work. Yet, the irony in that is that more value is created when one focuses on purpose, not profit. The last will be first, if you will."[27]

"Once a business leader embraces the idea that leadership is the art of optimizing cooperation, everything changes. Human dignity takes a front seat. Why? Because treating others with dignity enhances cooperation. The common good sits right beside human dignity, because caring for those with whom one is entrusted and their community enhances cooperation."

"May I add a thought or two here?" requested Brother Mark.

"Sure."

"In Catholic social teaching, the terms universal destination of goods,[28] solidarity,[29] and subsidiarity[30] are profound. I can see how

---

27 The Holy Bible, Matthew 20:16, (RSV), "So the last will be first, and the first last."
28 Blessed John Paul II, Encyclical Letter Laborem Exercens,14. ". . . the right to private property is subordinated to the right to common use, to the fact that goods are meant for everyone."
29 Blessed John Paul II, Encyclical Letter, Solicitudo Rei Socialis, 38. ". . . it is a firm and persevering determination to commit oneself to the common good. That is to say to the good of all and of each individual, because we are all really responsible for all. . . . a commitment to the good of one's neighbor with the readiness, in the gospel sense, to 'lose oneself' for the sake of the other instead of exploiting him, and to 'serve him' instead of oppressing him for one's own advantage."
30 The Catechism of the Catholic Church, 1883. "Excessive intervention by the state can threaten personal freedom and initiative. The teaching of the Church has elaborated the principle of subsidiarity, according to which 'a community of a higher order should not interfere in the internal life of a community of a lower order, depriving the latter of its functions, but rather should support it in case of need and help to coordinate its activity with the activities of the rest of society, always with a view to the common good.'" (Pius XI, Quadragesimo Anno I, 184-186)

each of these practiced in business would enhance cooperation. For instance, recognizing that though private property rights are critical to the proper functioning of free markets, goods are to be treated as if, ultimately, they are God's to be used for His purposes and the good of all mankind. By solidarity, we mean we are all in this together, even those in need and impoverished. And by subsidiarity, that there is value in decisions being made by those most directly affected and knowledgeable of the consequences of a decision. The practice of each of these at work would enhance cooperation."

"Yes! So now the activities to which a business leader tends and the decisions he or she makes are more fully aligned with the teachings of the Church, and, they result in more value creation for all, helping a business thrive in a free market."

Brother Mark reclined in his chair. Rebecca sat down. They both looked at the board in silence.

"So what do you think?" Rebecca looked at Brother Mark.

"I think this is amazing! And let me tell you why," Brother Mark proposed.

Rebecca sat up to listen and reached for the other cupcake.

"In his encyclical, *Caritas in Veritate*, Benedict XVI, called for 'a profoundly new way of understanding the business enterprise.'[31] I think you may have created a new business model; one that is results-oriented, and faith-integrated."

"We."

"What?" questioned Brother Mark.

"We may have created a new business model." Brother Mark accepted Rebecca's amendment.

---

31 Benedict XVI, op. cit.

"This model has huge implications in bringing those in business who claim their faith, but show little in practice at work, back to God. Your journey is manifest evidence of its power."

"Yes, it is profound," confessed Rebecca. "But the real hurdle here is the conscious and courageous choice to abandon and reject the dominant ideology. Using the two gateways you illustrated and the fact that government intervention into free markets is inversely proportional to the practice of virtues at work, gives one who is looking for more purpose at work a fighting chance."

Brother Mark listened.

"That is not an easy choice. To believe shareholders, a still significant stakeholder, are best served by business leaders concerning themselves with their people and their community will take some time to mature. But truth is on our side. This movement, if you will, must start with business leaders; those willing to choose a life of virtue at work over the life they currently live. If protecting free markets is a desired outcome for business leaders, then this is the price only business leaders can pay for the benefits thereof. Nothing is free."

Rebecca recited, "To whom much is given, much will be required."[32]

The Board Meeting

The next nine months flew by and Cupcakes and Coffee continued its long run of growth and profitability. Rebecca and Brother Mark continued their consulting relationship, though less frequently as both went about their business with a new understanding and appreciation of their roles as leaders.

The first annual shareholder's meeting of Cupcakes and Coffee was minutes from beginning in New York City. Both Rebecca and Brother Mark were there.

---

32 The Holy Bible, Luke 12:48 (ESV)

The meeting room at the Waldorf Astoria was packed with hundreds of shareholders and the media. The noise of varied conversations filled the air. Rebecca looked out to view the audience before she stepped to the podium to address those gathered. She had her script down, but was nervous none-the-less.

Kyle Masterson stood at the podium, waiting for a courteous lull in the conversations. "Ladies and gentlemen, we call the first annual shareholder's meeting of Cupcakes and Coffee, a publicly-traded company on the New York Stock Exchange to order. Please welcome the CEO of Cupcakes and Coffee, Mrs. Rebecca Morton."

Rebecca stepped on stage to address the quieting crowd as the applause died down.

"First of all, I would like to thank you all for being here. It has been a pleasure serving you and the company this last year; our first year as a publicly-traded company. The adjustment from being privately-held to publicly-traded is not an easy transition, but I believe we have done this well, and the results bear that out."

A smattering of applause echoed in the room.

"Each of you were given a copy of our annual report when you came into the room. The year-end financial statements and related 10K have been filed with the SEC as required by law. I trust each of you can review the financial statements, the earnings per share growth, the diluted earnings per share, the price-earnings ratio trends, and other financial measures of the company as time allows. As investors, you deserve a significant return on your investment, and I believe the company has delivered that, in spite of the very difficult pressures on business imposed by the passage of numerous laws that undoubtedly increase the cost of doing business."

A wave of incoherent mumbles crossed the room. Rebecca took this as a sign of solidarity for her previous comment.

"While our forecast for next fiscal year looks strong, there are continuing pressures to compete, control costs, and maintain our product pricing while we grow; and we do intend to grow. But I want to make you aware of significant other priorities of the company that I believe will create greater value for you in the future, and allow business to do the good that God intended for it to do." There, she had said it herself; in public, no less.

The crowd mumbled again, but returned to silence.

"Leading a business is both a blessing and a curse. It is a choice taken all too lightly for the potential upside, but blind to the downside or burden of doing so. The downside of which I speak is not poor financial results. It's the responsibility all businesses have to care for those with whom they are entrusted and concern themselves with the well being of those in need within their community. Cupcakes and Coffee has done this and will continue to do this."

Some applause came from the audience.

"This sounds like public relations rhetoric, I know. But allow me to explain how you can expect to see this burden manifested at Cupcakes and Coffee and why, I believe it will increase value for all stakeholders, including you."

The room was quiet.

"Our newest Board Member, Brother Mark Sculley, elected yesterday, and I have worked together all year to ensure value creation for all." Rebecca gestured toward Brother Mark to stand.

Brother Mark rose and waived to some applause. He stood out in the crowd wearing his black habit.

"The intrusiveness of the laws passed by the government this year caused us to really explore the nature of free markets, the intentions of government by intervening therein, and the dominant ideology that the purpose of business is to maximize shareholder wealth. Our exploration has revealed great truths. I'd like to share these with you, because it is based upon these truths that you can expect Cupcakes and Coffee to operate."

Rebecca panned the room to see that the audience was sitting, attentive, and ready. A single pre-prepared slide appeared behind Rebecca on the screen to assist the audience in following along with the truths that were about to be revealed.

"The first truth is that free markets offer the best opportunity for creating value for all. We must all commit ourselves to the protection of free markets, private property rights, and the rule of law that provide for the proper functioning of a free market."

"The second truth is that wealth is generated on the heels of significant value creation. This wealth is a blessing, yet opens up those blessed with it to a plethora of temptations and perversions that can destroy the benefits of a free market. Greed is not the least of these perversions."

The audience mumbled incoherently.

"The third truth is that government intervenes, independent of the politics, with the intention of righting injustices that are all too commonly observed in and/or caused in business. You can read any periodical and witness the scandals and controversies born from any number of these perversions."

"The fourth truth is that justice is, first, the responsibility of business leaders, not the government. Government responds where business leaders do not tend to their role to protect the human dignity of each person with whom they are entrusted, and where the common good is potentially threatened or diminished."

"The fifth truth is that we, as business leaders; I, am flawed and find it very difficult to withstand the temptations and perversions of wealth without my faith practiced every day. The cardinal virtues of temperance, wisdom, justice, and courage are critical to me tending to my proper role as CEO of this company. I commit to you that I will seek to practice and employ these in my daily life and in my role as CEO of Cupcakes and Coffee."

Brother Mark could not believe what he was hearing at a shareholder's meeting in New York City; what many think of as the center of and icon of capitalism.

"The sixth truth is that a business leader practicing the virtues at work is more effective at getting others to cooperate fully and willingly in the work at hand. This is the essence of effective leadership, and when two people work together they get a better return for their work than any one person can. Effective leadership, in this way, generates enhanced value."

"Enhanced value generates more wealth. More wealth requires more virtue. More virtue practiced at work diminishes the need for government to intervene and fuels excellent leadership, which generates enhanced value, more wealth, the need for more virtue . . . and the cycle continues. Shareholders benefit. Employees benefit. Our communities benefit. Government tends to its role doing only what it can and is supposed to do."

Some affirmative applause came from the audience.

"In this logical cycle, there is a price for business leaders to pay; a price for me to pay. While I, and the Company, will honor and recognize you as shareholders, each of you investing your hard-earned wealth in Cupcakes and Coffee in anticipation of a return, you are not the sole beneficiary of the good that God intended business to do. So I have chosen to label the dominant ideology as flawed and commit myself to living a life of virtue, for the sake of the employees who serve our customers every day, for the sake of those serving those who serve customers every day, for the sake of those in our community who have suffered from injustice and deserve better, and for the purpose of mitigating the intervention of government into areas where we business leaders are wholly accountable, bringing greater value to you, our shareholders. A life of virtue is the price only business leaders can pay to protect the value born of free markets." With increased emphasis and meter, Rebecca finished. "I will pay that price."

A voice from the back yelled, "Here, here!" After a brief pause, applause started at the back of the room and rolled forward like a tidal wave. Someone in the fourth row of tables stood up and like a pebble dropped into a puddle of water, the audience stood and applauded Rebecca's personal confession and commitment as CEO of Cupcakes and Coffee.

Humbled and honored, Rebecca politely nodded her head in affirmation of the courageous choice she had made; a choice and price only business leaders can pay.

Epilogue

The news press, television and radio all picked up on Rebecca's address at the shareholder's meeting. It was front page news in the Wall Street Journal, USA Today, and The Kansas City Star. The Today Show and GMA both covered the address in their national news segment. Invitations from all over the country poured into Rebecca's office requesting campus visits and speeches.

She landed a second GMA interview, and chose to bring Marj, Carrie, and Liz with her on the trip. They all got to meet Josh.

Rebecca's address to shareholders became the stuff of legends over the next five years. The new way to think about a business enterprise became adopted by, first, a handful of companies, then hundreds, and now over a thousand. There is a true business Renaissance occurring in America. Business is more competitive on the world stage as people are cooperating more in the work. Our communities are safer and growing as business embraces the holistic health of their greater community. The words God and business don't sound so strange together anymore as business leaders root each other on to the good God intended for business to do.

Government remains of the people, by the people, and for the people; doing what only it can do; intervening in business only when necessary to reinforce private property rights and the rule of law. Business has a confidence in the U.S. free market. Capital is flowing and business leaders are deploying it wisely. Leverage is at reasonable levels.

More and more people are finding out that the practice of virtues at work is difficult and a steep price to pay to lead business in a free market. But the rewards are substantial, both quantitatively and qualitatively. Many have found the strength through their faith and have reengaged meaningfully with God and their Church communities.

Rebecca has remained focused on leading Cupcakes and Coffee, a still publicly-traded company, through the whims of the stock market, though, the real value created by the company has remained consistent and upwards. She continues to follow through on the promise to pay the price only business leaders can pay to protect free markets, that from which she, and many others, have been so richly blessed.

The End

The Model

It's time for a new way of understanding the business enterprise and the good it can do. Here is one perspective on the good God intended for business to do.

"God destined the earth and all it contains for all men and all peoples so that all created things would be shared fairly by all mankind under the guidance of justice tempered by charity."[33] The principle of the universal destination of goods is an invitation to develop an economic vision inspired by moral values that permit people not to lose sight of the origin or purpose of these goods, so as to bring about a world of fairness and solidarity, in which the creation of wealth can take on a positive function. Wealth, in effect, presents the possibility in the many different forms in which it can find expression as the result of a process of production that works with the available technological and economic resources, both natural and derived. This result is guided by resourcefulness, planning and labor, and used as a means for promoting the well-being of all men and all peoples and for preventing their exclusion and exploitation.[34]

An enterprise that produces a product or service of value to others; enough that others will exchange what they have of value for what you have of value; multiplied thousands of times, can create benefits for an entire society. Business enterprises employ people in the value creation process providing an opportunity for those working to exchange their skills for value, and, in turn, exchange value they've earned for other items of value that improve their quality of life. We in America have lived this.

---

33 Pastoral Constitution *Gaudium et Spes*, 69: AAS 58 (1966), 1090.
34 *Compendium*, op. cit., 174, 76.

A market economy like this inherently invites some inequality between the value created and property owned by different people. This inequality can spawn a set of temptations and perversions that serve to diminish the perceived benefits of this economic model.

In another economic model, property can be either jointly owned and/or centrally distributed. This model promises more equality in property owned, but fails to delivery on its promise. Because a third party is required to determine who gets what, without the requisite knowledge or ability to assess true needs, entitlement in others and corruption in the third party are invited.

History has proven the consequences of both economic models. Free markets are the best model for creating value. Where an enterprise is really good at creating value, wealth is generated if value received is greater than the cost incurred. In accounting terms, the wealth generated in the form of net profit, can be either retained by the enterprise for use to create more value, or can be distributed through distributions or dividend payments to investors who put capital at risk in hopes of generating a return. Where value exchanged is less than the cost incurred, wealth is diminished and the value provider is destined to either change the outcome or stop the attempt to create value; they go out of business.

Wealth generation is the outcome of significant value creation. The accumulation of that wealth is tempting and can become an end in-and-of-itself without regard for others or the community in which we live. This use of wealth is virtually condoned, if not invited by the dominant ideology that the purpose of business is to maximize shareholder value – a single-stakeholder perspective. It is so institutionalized now in the thinking of business people that many business leaders feel justified in doing things that awaken public antagonists and warrant some form of mitigating response. For lack of a better, inside-business alternative, the default response is government intervention.

Absent any other form of temperance or justice, the government or State is left to intervene when the generation of profits creates a set of temptations that lead to perversions in practice. The government, well intended, initiates programs aimed at caring for the marginalized in society; the hungry; the poor; the oppressed, tending to their role as the protector, insurer, and flag-bearer of the common good. Yet by doing so for extended periods of time, they do harm; inviting an entitlement mind-set, among other things.

The premise that government exists to protect human dignity and insure the common good is thought by some to be as erroneous as the idea that business exists to do good. The motives of politicians can come into question just as much as those of business leaders. This model is for business leaders, independent of motivations of politicians who enact legislation that negates the rule of law required for free markets.

There is another instrument of justice and temperance that is intended to presuppose government intervention; the practice of virtues by business people. To the extent the practice of virtues is absent in business, government is left to fill the void. Herein lies the challenge for business leaders..

The idea that a well-developed set of virtues can supplant government intervention as the means by which the common good is manifested is not disagreeable to most business people. The idea that the two are inversely proportional makes sense. What is more difficult to fathom is how a business run with this belief system can win in a competitive marketplace.

There is an unwanted, unintended consequence of the nominal practice of virtues in the marketplace. Business leaders absent virtues or a foundational set of principles intended for good, too often execute random acts of management that serve to diminish cooperation and encourage individual achievement over that of the whole. A person working in an environment like this tends to disengage more from the work, working only for a paycheck. Supervision is required to insure compliance. The lack of trust impairs speed of response and agility. Costs increase. Protection of status becomes the norm instead of achievement of results. Value creation diminishes.

A virtuous leader in business is attractive to others. Employees tend to follow a person who is wise, tempered, courageous, and just. Sure the underlying business model and strategy must be sound for success in a competitive marketplace, but when all other things are equal, the business leader who has a team that is fully and willingly committed to the work at hand, wins.

The practice of virtues is often interpreted and practiced as generous and charitable giving post-profit or once profits are distributed to owners. Business owners do well by giving generously to causes that serve those in need or that help further humanitarian or societal causes. But there is an unintended consequence of this practice in the form of a missed opportunity. Virtues in the practice of business, not just on the heels of distributed wealth, serve to fuel the cooperative effort and commitment of employees; that which results in significant competitive advantage.

Cooperation speaks to the purpose and essence of leadership. A business leader who can build talent and accomplish results through the cooperation of others creates a competitive advantage that is hard to emulate and near impossible to duplicate. In this way, the practice of virtues becomes the vehicle by which the force and commitment of many compete and win in the marketplace, further enhancing value creation.

Some will argue leadership defined as the art of optimizing cooperation is just another soft, warm-and-fuzzy means of taking the hard edges off those leading a business. Enhancing cooperation undoubtedly requires a belief system that concerns itself with those doing the work, yet the continuum of leadership decisions made to insure that cooperation is enhanced mandates identification of problems, quick intervention, honest accountability, proper use of discipline, and continuous building of trust, among many other important leadership practices. Leadership as the art of optimizing cooperation is the bridge between the practices of virtues and increased value creation. The practice of virtues when leading a business enhances the cooperative effort and strengthens an enterprise's competitive advantage in the marketplace.

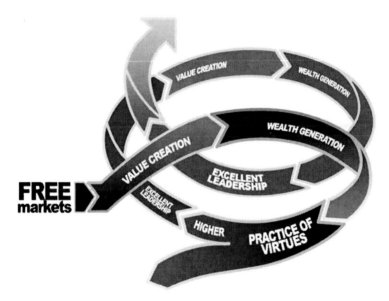

This virtues-centered business model in which results matter is critical to the evolution of business. It demands that business leaders practice an ever-increasing level of virtues in the workplace to enhance cooperation and to mitigate the temptations and perversions of wealth generation that come on the heels of value creation; the product of free markets. Living a virtuous life is the price only business leaders can pay to protect the benefits of free markets.

If we want to live and work in a country where people have the opportunity to experience liberty and justice for all, then business leaders must pay this price.

Will you?

Virtues-Centered Business Model

© 2013 Dave Geenens

Acknowledgements

There are many people to thank for the product which is this book. It's been 30-years in the making; matching the span of my work career so far. Many business leaders have invested in me and shared wisdom and insights into life, work, and faith. For those who have led me and worked with me, I owe a huge debt of gratitude. Thank you!

This book, though, is truly the next step in a quest to illuminate how one's faith must be part of one's work and leadership. In the last four years, I have been blessed to work at Benedictine College, where people have challenged me to think about, and not just 'do' the practice of business and to assess the benefits of free markets. Thank you to the entire faculty and staff at Benedictine College. You have been patient to listen and slow to judge.

As I developed the characters and settings in which the tenets of the book would be revealed and practiced, many real people from the College, St. Benedict's Abbey, and the town of Atchison occupied my mind's eye. Thank you for letting me stealthily consider your being as the story unfolded. Any resemblance to a real person is, nevertheless, coincidental. On the other hand, Nell Hills, Jerry's Again, Benedictine College and St. Benedict's Abbey are real places in the real town of Atchison in northeast Kansas. Come visit!

Many people took the time to read and edit the original manuscript. Others read the book draft for pleasure and shared their thoughts and encouragement. For their investment in this project, I acknowledge Kevin Lowry, Dr. John Settich, Steve Minnis, John Joerger, Kelly Vowels, John Menghini, Dr. Rick Coronado, Brother Luke Turner, and Mike Stec, among others.

Thank you to Erin Venable with Loft43 for her creativity and graphic design work on the virtues-centered model graphic and the book cover.

Thank you to my wife, Terry, and my children (now adults), Megan, Aubrey, and Austin, for the room and margin to do what I do.

God's plan for redemption and the sending of his one and only son, Jesus Christ, to the earth to bear witness to the truth is amazing! I must correct myself, though. There is one thing that is truly free to you and to me, because the price has already been paid. God paid it for us through the sacrifice of his son, Jesus Christ, for our sins.

That which is free is now priceless as we pursue a life of virtue. I acknowledge this truth and am thankful that God loves me in spite of my missteps and misgivings. I pray you receive this gift, as well.

Other Books by Dave Geenens

LEADERSLIP | ISBN 978-0-9816017-5-5

Published in 2010, this book challenges leaders to rescue their enterprises and wake up to the revolution that is upon us. The 'Zoomers,' the generational bands following the 'Boomers,' are going to force changes in leadership.

This is a very practical read with numerous models, tools, and case studies that will help any enterprise leader improve results. But it requires a new understanding of leadership and the courage to navigate far from where we are today in American enterprise leadership.

❝With the changing workforce, the premise of Dave Geenens' book is accurate. He asserts we need a new type of leadership in the 21st Century and outlines a plan to get us there. Dave's wealth of experience as an executive lends credibility to his writing. It is a practical and must read for the 21st Century leader.❞

–**Karen Black,** Insight Edge Executive Coaching and Consulting

---

ARISE! | ISBN 0-9768210-0-1

This was Dave's original work regarding a new framework for leadership; Cooperative Competency©. The book is a personal testimony of life and a career lived in search of something better. Dave shares his frustrations with what is and makes a case for leadership of a different kind.

Dave weaves Biblical truth into the framework for those who share his frustration with current leadership practice and provides a strong foundation for leadership that optimizes cooperation and, ultimately, results for all stakeholders.

❝*ARISE!* is a hard-hitting, honest look at the state of business leadership today and how leaders willing to live their faith at work can produce yet unforeseen results in their enterprise and find the peace and confidence of living a life of integrity.❞

–**Greg Hatcher,** President, The Hatcher Agency, Little Rock, AR

135